MINISTER and DOCTOR MEET

Harper & Brothers, Publishers, New York

MINISTER
and DOCTOR
MEET

by Granger E. Westberg

To my eighteen-year-old daughter Jane
who

encouraged me to finish this book
gave up her summer vacation to type
and retype the manuscript
made many suggestions regarding both
style and content which I heeded
daily gives me reason to have confidence
in today's youth

CONTENTS

Introduction

Ministers and doctors meet each other daily in hospitals all across the land. This book is concerned about the fact that they seldom meet each other on a really professional level. The sick patient is the focus of attention for both of them, yet the doctor as scientist and the minister as philosopher or theologian somehow think that their respective tasks have little relationship to each other. Whenever they try to converse they find communication difficult because each looks at the patient's problem from his own perspective. The daily greeting of ministers and doctors, therefore, needs to be changed into a "meeting" which would benefit them and the patient as well.

We are beginning to see that neither the doctor nor the minister can do his best work in isolation from the other. Our new appreciation of the holistic (which ought to be, and in this book will be, spelled with a "w": wholistic) approach to the problems of man has reminded us that the whole is equal to more than just the sum of its parts. For a time each of us thought we could best accomplish our ends by working intensively in our own area. Now we are not sure of this. If man is an indivisible entity and if the doctor and the minister have dedicated their lives to serving him in times of crisis, then we had better get together for a continuing discussion of our basic philosophy, our goals, and our methods.

As a physician analyzes his relationship with his patients, he finds that a portion of each day is devoted to the practice of the *science* of medicine and another portion to the *art* of medicine. In the latter he is aware of the delicate texture of human relationships, which are so important in the healing process. What is true of the doctor is also true of the pastor. The minister's education seeks to develop his understanding of the Christian faith in such a way that he can share it effectively with others. But if he is to be genuinely helpful to the people he serves, he must also be concerned with the *art* of pastoral care—that delicate human relationship between pastor and parishioner in which religious growth occurs.

Those doctors and clergymen who have been comparing notes over the past two decades have been struck by the amazing similarity between the *art* of medicine and the *art* of pastoral care. In these pages we will seek to explore these areas of common interest with the frank hope that physicians will want to encourage clergymen to participate actively in the health program. A large portion of this book is devoted to a description of how the minister works with people in stress, because a physician can hardly be expected to invite the minister to join with him until he understands and approves what the pastor does.

It is certain that physicians reading this book will raise some stimulating questions concerning the place of the minister in the community health program. I would appreciate hearing such reactions so that subsequent writing will have the benefit of their suggestions. This field of interco-operation is so new and our experiments so few that it will be particularly gratifying if small groups of physicians and ministers across the country will seek to test the basic thesis developed in this book. The thesis might be stated this way: it is possible for physicians and clergymen to work with each other on a professional level if they begin by discussing jointly the whole person—the patient. We believe that the results of this ongoing study and conversation will be beneficial to the patient.

Much that is said here is based on the work currently in progress at the University of Chicago. I am particularly grateful for the stimulation of my colleague Professor Seward Hiltner, who for ten years was chairman of the field of Religion and Personality of the Theological Faculty of the University. Dr. Hiltner has written much in the area of pastoral care and psychiatry, and among his many unusual responsibilities he serves as a consultant

for the Menninger Foundation in Topeka, Kansas. I am also indebted to Dr. Lowell T. Coggeshall of the Medical School and
Dean Jerald Brauer of the Theological Faculty for their vision
and encouragement in building a "bridge" between the medical
school and the divinity school. Although these schools have been
only three hundred feet apart on the Midway campus, they could
just as well have been three hundred miles apart. Today this
situation is changing. It is gratifying to see theological and medical students sit together in religion-medicine case conferences on
our campus to discuss how their two perspectives may be
brought to bear on the problems of man's total health.

My particular task as Associate Professor of Religion and
Health is unusually challenging because this is a joint appointment on both the medical and theological faculties. Such an
appointment affords considerable freedom to move back and forth
between these two disciplines in an attempt to discover natural
ways in which the professions can become aware of the many
areas in which their functions overlap. In the process of testing
various means of bringing about interprofessional co-operation
we have used four methods which hold promise for our work
and which we hope will be tested in other medical centers. The
methods we regularly employ include: (a) The appointment of
theological students as part-time chaplains in the medical center
where they are assigned to medical and surgical services and make
rounds with physicians. In this work they are also supervised by
teaching chaplains related to the theological faculty. (b) Religion-
medicine case conferences open to an interdisciplinary group in
which case studies of hospital patients are presented jointly by
medical interns and student chaplains who have co-operatively
dealt with a patient's problem. (c) Elective courses and general
lectures for medical students on the interrelationship of religion
and medicine. (d) Experimental pilot projects off campus where
our thesis regarding the value of interprofessional co-operation is
tested in community situations with physicians and clergy who
are in active practice.

Because my experience was not too different from that of a

number of parish pastors who have gradually moved into a hospital setting, I have tried in the first chapter to describe how I found myself in the field of health service. My own interest in religion and health covers approximately the same period in which so many changes have taken place across the country in hospitals of all types in relation to the spiritual care of their patients. Recently the American Hospital Association approved the establishment of a committee on Hospital Chaplaincies in order to answer the increasing number of requests from nonchurch hospitals which plan to inaugurate chaplaincy programs. As I have tried to describe my own experiences the reader can be certain that other hospital chaplains have had many like them and that there are probably hundreds of other parish pastors who will be going into the hospital ministry during the next two decades. While only about 20 per cent of hospitals now have full-time chaplains on their staffs, it is the opinion of hospital administrators that this number will triple during the next ten years.

PART I

The Patient: Focus of Doctor and Minister

CHAPTER 1

How I Found Myself in the Field of Health

When I became a parish minister, it was my plan that when any one of my parishioners became ill, I would go to his physician and offer my services in a "team approach" to illness. Since no one had ever spelled it out for me I was not exactly sure what this team was to do, but I had a vague feeling that somehow the physician and the minister belonged together. When a parishioner went to the hospital a few days after I was installed in my first parish, I proceeded to call her doctor. As nearly as I can remember, the conversation went something like this: "Dr. Smith? One of my parishioners, Mrs. Johnson, is your patient and before I go to the hospital to call on her, I wonder if there is anything you think I might be able to do that would be of help." There was a long silence at the other end of the line. When Dr. Smith had caught his breath, he said: "Well, ah...I don't know anything about your business, Reverend. I make it a point to keep off the subject of religion. I can't tell you how to run your affairs." This pretty well finished the conversation and I knew there would be no point in calling him again.

When a second parishioner became ill, I summoned my courage and made a personal call at the doctor's office. Unable to understand the purpose of my call, the receptionist listed me as a new patient. The doctor gave me a warm welcome, but when I told him my mission, he said, "Oh, I don't think of anything in particular you can do for Mrs. Blank. Just pray for her. Everybody can stand a prayer now and then, don't you think?" I could see our interview was over, and I sensed that it was because most doctors and ministers have never learned to recognize and to understand the areas in which their work overlaps. They have not known what to say to each other regarding professional matters. Nevertheless, it bothered me to think that when my people were sick, I was not considered a member of the healing team. The doctor thought my work concerned "religion"—a system of praying, churchgoing, doctrines, and dogmas, which had nothing to do with the day-to-day problems confronting sick persons.

Of course, I could not justifiably blame him. At that time it was commonly agreed that the physician was a scientist who worked on the body, while the minister was a type of philosopher who cared for the soul. Because people had done such a good job dividing man into these parts, it logically followed that the physician and the minister were dealing with two utterly separate aspects of man.

However, it still did not seem right to me that the physician and the minister should be miles apart in their thinking when they spent so much time in hospitals dealing with the same people. The thought kept recurring that maybe they ought to get acquainted —on a professional level. Unfortunately, I had not the slightest notion of how to go about this.

Co-operation at any depth seemed to necessitate a background of research and communication on the basic philosophical interpenetration of each discipline. But even as I write these lines some twenty years later this kind of research is only beginning. A further problem was that during our respective educations there was no hint as to the possibility of interdisciplinary communication on a professional level. Theology and medicine were totally isolated from each other. Thus, to attempt a truly integrated co-operation between two men required more than their personal willingness.

With a fumbling determination to develop some conversation between minister and doctor, I continued trying to talk personally with doctors about patients who were our common concern

—still without success. Fortunately, I was getting to know several physicians socially and my wife and I enjoyed their company immensely. Occasionally, when a group of us were together in one of our homes, some tentative feelers regarding professional co-operation began to emerge, but the comments were brief and that was as far as it went. As I see it now, these preliminary ways of becoming acquainted helped to establish a mutual trust. This type of trust was necessary because then we felt secure enough to allow each other to ask the searching questions related to basic presuppositions of our respective groups.

It was about that time that I reread *The Art of Ministering to the Sick* by Dr. Richard C. Cabot of Harvard Medical School (now deceased) and Rev. Russell L. Dicks, then chaplain at Massachusetts General Hospital in Boston. In 1937 when I had first read the exciting description of new ways of ministering to people under stress, I was led to contemplate a "team approach" to the care of my parishioners. Now something had gone wrong and I was trying to find out what it was.

In rereading this book one factor became immediately clear: I needed to spend time analyzing my own work with my people. Dicks had developed an entirely new concept of studying the ways pastors talk with people. Previously clergymen had thought that a pastoral call was constituted of prayer and Scripture reading, not of conversation between pastor and parishioner. However, Dicks believed that the *entire conversation* could be pastoral and healing in nature. He showed that most pastors merely "visit" the sick and at the end of their stay they "tack on" a religious rite, totally irrelevant to the conversation or to the spiritual needs of the parishioner. In order to demonstrate this, Dicks had asked scores of seasoned pastors to write down conversations which they were having in the sickroom. A large percentage of these verbatim reports disclosed the following features: the pastor merely makes a "friendly visit" to the hospital, not a pastoral call; the visits are almost entirely "pastor centered," indicating indifference to the patients' needs; the minister has little or no knowledge as to his position on the healing team and the pastor's theological education prepared him to preach at people, not to counsel with them.

After finishing this book for the second time, I vowed to take a few minutes after each hospital call to reflect upon what had taken place. In some cases I decided to write down as much of the conversation as I could remember and then ask myself such questions as: Was this a patient-centered call or did I take over and talk about myself? After calling on this patient, do I know more about him? What were the themes of our discussion and why did the patient choose these? How does the patient perceive me and how do I plan to help him? In other words, why am I spending time with him unless something of benefit to him is taking place? As I sought to answer these questions, I realized that my answers were often inconclusive, vague, or unrealistic. At this point I decided I was not ready to participate with other professional people in the health field. First, I had to clarify my own role in ministering to the sick.

That is why I was pleased when a year or so later at a clergy conference I happened to sit at the same dinner table with the aged chaplain of a denominational hospital. In a comment meant to be facetious, he said, "I have to be away for a week next month. How about one of you men taking over while I'm gone?" This seemed like a wonderful opportunity to work closely with doctors and to try to answer my questions about doctor-minister co-operation, so I immediately volunteered.The chaplain chuckled and said, "I was only fooling." This, he said, was not a job for a young fellow in his twenties; the average age of hospital chaplains was seventy-seven. However, when the chaplain saw I was serious, he made arrangements for me to take over his duties for a week and to live in the medical interns' quarters.

The week as temporary chaplain at Augustana Lutheran Hospital of Chicago was one of the most fascinating periods of my life. As I entered this church-related hospital, I was impressed by the fact that there was no visible symbol to indicate that this institution was patterned after the kind of concern demonstrated long ago by the Great Physician. As I began making my rounds, I got the impression that the chaplain had so many people to see that if a patient had a real problem, the chaplain would have to say, "I'm sorry but I don't have time to talk with you now. I see that you are in real need. If I get through saying hello to all the people I am supposed to greet, I will try to get back to help you." The few hospital chaplains active in those days were under great pressure to turn in statistical reports. The groups which sponsored chaplains seemed to be more concerned with how many patients the chaplain saw rather than how well he attended to their needs.

At noon I went to the dining room for lunch and was told that the chaplain always sat at the head table with the superintendent. Throughout the meal the conversation centered around shop talk —administration, finances, buildings, and equipment. But I could overhear conversation about patients at a nearby doctors' table. Since this type of talk was of vital interest to me, I asked the superintendent if I might sit at one of the doctors' tables for the remainder of the week. "No," he replied, "I think you'd better not. The chaplain has sat at this table for fifty years." When I pressed him, he shook his head wisely and said, "I'm afraid the doctors would not care to have a clergyman at their table. You see," he added with hesitation, "their language isn't always the best." When I assured him I had heard a few rather expressive words in my life and could probably stand it for a week, he finally agreed that I might try it, but he was sure the doctors would not be pleased. It was as if he were throwing me to the wolves. I soon found out he was not far wrong.

At the next meal, I sat at one of their tables. I was wearing clerical attire, and a young resident turned to me and in a semi-friendly way said, "What in the —— are you doing here at this table?" I explained that I was there for a week to see how the church carried on its ministry of healing. His startled reply was, "Church? Its ministry of healing? The doctors do all the healing around here. The church just hires some tired old man to pass out tracts." Later in the conversation the doctor said, "I know the church has done a good job with buildings, equipment, and beds, but why doesn't it get more interested in doing something for the patients as people?"

For the remainder of the week I got less sleep and drank more coffee than during any other week of my life. I went on every emergency call, and as I would walk back to the interns' quarters with a young doctor he might say, "I sewed up the wound; what did you do, Chaplain?" Then I would try to describe the talk I had had with the parents of a teen-ager who had been injured in an auto accident. I told him how the father had blamed himself for the fact that his boy associated with a gang of hoodlums who often drove around town in search of excitement. In his introspective mood the father was admitting that he had never gone out of his way to develop a close relationship with his son. He said that just seeing a clergyman reminded him how he had erred in this regard, and he hoped he might have another opportunity to prove that he could be a better father.

This kind of discussion with the interns of what a minister does went on all week. It seemed that the hospital was alive with frightened people who had been stopped in their tracks for the first time in many years. They wanted to talk to someone who represented a power greater than themselves. They also wanted to sound out a clergyman to see if in their present dilemma God really cared about them. Here was a concentration of anxious, worried people, figuratively begging for someone to take a personal interest in them. During that one week, I saw more people who wanted to talk about vital matters than I had found in my church in several months.

When this exciting week ended I had the feeling that more serious thinking was taking place per square foot in a hospital than in any other building in the community—including the nearby college. I was also sure that if the church felt that the Christian faith had anything to say to people in time of trouble, the best place to have its pastors say it was in the context of suffering, anxiety, birth, and death. Where else could a minister find people so ready to talk about spiritual concerns? There is, perhaps, no better time or place to test the validity of the faith handed down to us than in the hospital setting.

When I returned home, I could scarcely think of anything but the church's responsibility in conducting its hundreds of outstanding hospitals. Was it aware of the tremendous opportunities in this setting where people were asking essentially theological questions? I could not resist writing up my impressions of this fascinating week and after some hesitation sent them to the hospital administrator. He was kind enough to read my letter at the next meeting of the board of directors. Two days later I received an appointment to a committee—a typical American gesture. This was to be a committee on the work of the chaplain. A few weeks later we met with the chaplain, and he was surprised to find that this group's purpose was to get acquainted with him and his work and to learn how they might give it more value in the hospital's life.

When he was asked what he would like to have the committee do for him, he said, "The first thing I would appreciate would be if I could carry on my work very much as I did when I was a parish pastor." (And he had been a very successful pastor.) "I would like the privilege of no longer having to fill out a statistical report indicating the number of people I have seen or the amount of literature I have passed out. Instead, I would like to feel free to stop at the bedside of those people for whom I feel I could be of some help and see them as often as necessary. This will mean that a number of people coming into this hospital will never have a visit from the chaplain, but I am not sure that every patient needs a visit as much as a few patients need more intensive pastoral care." The committee unanimously adopted the chaplain's suggestion.

During the following three years, I was in regular communication with the hospital and its life and I found myself intrigued by the many facets of its service to humanity. In 1943 a severe illness caused the retirement of the chaplain. Our committee was asked to select a new chaplain, "a young man in his late sixties or early seventies." Each man we approached—and I must admit we went down into the fifties—was insulted to be considered for this position because it implied that we thought he was ready for retirement or that he was doing an inadequate job in the parish and therefore ought to take a less demanding hospital position. As I sought to persuade each candidate to consider the hospital chaplaincy seriously, I was, in effect, also talking to myself. When one man after another turned down the position, I came to the realization that this field of service was acutely misunderstood. "Why should this work be limited to older men? Wouldn't the hospital offer a challenge to a younger man?"

It was not long before my whole being was stirred by what I considered the remarkable potential for pastoral care in a hospital setting. During my week as temporary chaplain I had talked with many people whose illness forced them for the first time in years to raise basic religious questions. It did not seem right that only retired clergymen should be given the opportunity to serve in such a capacity. True, such men could draw upon a wealth of past experience, but unfortunately, church hospitals were taking advantage of these older men because they provided an inexpensive way to solve the chaplaincy problem. With their meager pensions the retired ministers needed part-time work to supplement their incomes. Furthermore, by hiring these men, the hospital was indicating only a token interest in the religious dimensions of the healing ministry. As long as the hospital had a chaplain, it fulfilled the letter of the law. When these older men had new ideas or suggestions for improving the spiritual care of the patient, they were often told that their jobs were only temporary and therefore they should not begin a project which they might not be around to complete. My objection, then, had nothing to do with older men per se, but with the fact that they were inadvertently blocking any development of new ideas by alert young clergymen who would be active long enough to carry out their projects.

After our committee had received refusals from half a dozen candidates and was wondering where to turn next, I found myself so bothered by the situation that I blurted out, "Have you fellows ever thought of me?" Obviously they had not and they considered this to be humorous indeed. It took me a long time to convince them I was serious, but they finally called me, and I took one school year to prepare for the work.

My decision to become a hospital chaplain was perhaps hardest on my mother. For fully five years people would say to her, "Mrs. Westberg, what happened to your boy?" or "Mrs. Westberg, will Granger get a parish again someday?" One pastor solemnly grasped her hand and said, "I'm so sorry to hear that your son has left the ministry."

Today people are only slowly being convinced that a clergyman is just as much in the ministry when he serves as a hospital chaplain as when he is a parish pastor. Actually, it can be demonstrated that the chaplain devotes more time each day ministering to the inner needs of people than a parish pastor does. The chaplain spends almost no time on the mechanics of running a parish —raising funds, or building up the membership, organizing committees, keeping the choir in harmony, or dozens of other chores related to the parish. The chaplaincy is such a rewarding pastoral experience that undoubtedly some of the most promising clergymen will be taking an additional year of postgraduate study to qualify as professional hospital chaplains.

The hospital chaplaincy movement is gaining momentum each year. When a handful of us organized the first Association of Hospital Chaplains in 1945, we did not dream that within a few years over three hundred qualified chaplains would have positions in the leading hospitals of the country.

Clinical training for clergymen dates back to the early 1920's when a Congregational minister, Anton T. Boisen, became mentally ill and was taken to the Worcester State Hospital in Massachusetts. In his delirium he called for a chaplain, but there was none. He begged to talk to someone who might be able to understand what was going on inside him, for he felt that this terrifying experience could best be understood and described in religious terms. In more lucid moments, Boisen wrote down some of his feelings about the interrelationship of mental illness and religious experience. When he was released two years later, he sought to convince the hospital administration of the value of the chaplain's role in ministering to mental patients. It seems incredible that a former patient could immediately persuade his doctors to do something about the lack of religious care in their hospital. But within a short time, Anton Boisen became chaplain of this hospital, marking the beginning of his leadership in the clinical training movement within theological education and more generally in religion and psychiatry.

From the first, Chaplain Boisen saw the value of bringing young theological students into his hospital to serve part time as orderlies and part time as chaplains. In this way they could acquire information about the dynamics of human behavior through direct observation of extreme cases. He invited these students to the hospital's three-month course in clinical pastoral care which he inaugurated, in which psychiatrists, physicians, and social workers worked closely with the students and pointed out the ways in which they, as clergymen, could be of assistance to the mentally disturbed. This movement caught the imagination of hundreds of theological students and soon other students were invited to serve as student chaplains in both general hospitals and mental hospitals.

In the 1930's a similar movement began in the general hospitals under the inspiration of Dr. Richard C. Cabot and the leadership of Rev. Russell L. Dicks, whom we have mentioned earlier. Also, as a result of the work of Boisen, Dicks, and many others, two groups for the advancement of clinical pastoral training came into being: the Council for Clinical Training and the Institute of Pastoral Care. Both groups are vigorous in their work and have attracted the attention of theological professors to the degree that almost every seminary in the country has taken clinical training seriously. The idea of clinical training was enthusiastically received, first in the East and then in the Midwest. In the setting of mental and general hospitals and penal institutions, clergymen and seminarians could study for three or more months under a teaching chaplain and in close connection with the medical and psychiatric staff. When seminary faculty members began to see the value of summers spent in the clinic studying what Boisen termed "the living human document," they encouraged their students to take such work. Now a number of seminaries require students to spend one or more summers relating what they have received in the classroom to the clinical study of people under stress. The fact that hospitals provide a multiprofessional setting also gives the student an early acquaintance with other professional people with whom he will have occasion to work during the rest of his professional life.

CHAPTER 2

The Professional Conversation
"All I did was to talk to him."

By the very nature of their work, the doctor and the minister are involved in almost constant conversation with people who reveal to them their innermost thoughts. Both the doctor and the minister frequently comment, "All I did was talk to him," as if this were not a very important part of their work. Often the doctor's patient ostensibly comes for another purpose—to have a physical checkup, or to get more pills. Parishioners do the same thing. They supposedly come to talk to the minister about the Men's Club project or the Ladies' Aid supper, but if they find him in a receptive mood, they will move on to subjects nearer to their own needs.

The physician and the minister do not think of themselves as counselors in the professional sense, yet what they pass off as mere conversation is, for the person seeking them out, serious counseling. A well-known national magazine titled one of its most impelling full-page advertisements, "Why some voices carry more weight than others." Then it went on to say, "A young boy hangs on his dad's every word. You sit up and take notice when your doctor or lawyer tells you something. The fact is: *who* says it is every bit as important as *what* is said."

Men in such respected fields as medicine and religion have an obligation to be acutely aware of what they say and how they say it. Those who have been doing considerable research on the art of conversation state that these brief conversations can be much more therapeutic than they are now. Until recently medical and divinity schools have placed little or no emphasis on the art of communication. For instance, the average seminary curriculum seemed to imply that the ability to preach to a congregation was more important than the ability to discuss a religious problem with an individual. Even though there is such apparent disinterest among most postgraduate faculties, no one can overlook the fact that patients and parishioners consider a personal conversation with their doctor or minister to be directly related to professional care.

Such an interview is an unusual experience which for the average person takes place only once in two to five years. He will often quote "what the doctor (or minister) said" to his friends for months afterward. Professional men should not be expected to develop the art of counseling by just picking it up along the way. The danger of getting into permanently unhelpful habits is too great. Fortunately, the number of postgraduate courses in this area is increasing so that all of those who talk with people may be brought up to date on the newest insights into the dynamics of interpersonal relationships.

When doctors and ministers have permitted their office conversations to be recorded and analyzed, they have found this helpful in discovering the strengths and weaknesses in their personal interactions with people who come to them. In order to make these brief conversations therapeutic, it is well to understand something of the basic theory of what is involved when two people seek to communicate with each other. For too long conversation has been taken for granted—anyone can do it—and now it is becoming clearer that much more is happening in this process than was previously realized. The study of what is happening is quite a well-developed science which needs to be taken seriously by all who engage in it.

It would be convenient if conversations in the doctor's office could be classified under the headings of medical or nonmedical problems. However, the absurdity of this thought is clear when it is realized that no problem is purely medical, for the human relationship between the doctor and patient is always significant. Certainly there are some problems where this relationship is less crucial. Even if the doctor displays little personal regard for the patient, in some cases the physical treatment will be quite effective. However, this very impersonality might cause the treatment of another type of individual to fail. As soon as the doctor must deal with the patient as a person, the crucial factor becomes the effectiveness or the ineffectiveness of the interpersonal relationship.

When a patient comes with a predominantly physical problem, it is as if he were bringing his body to the doctor. After analyzing the symptoms, the doctor, on the basis of his knowledge of physiology, anatomy, and chemistry, proceeds to prescribe what he considers to be best for the patient. Thus while the patient plays a somewhat passive role, the doctor helps him with various drugs and therapies.

When the patient comes with a functional problem, the doctor must put that patient in a different role. (Functional illness usually means that bodily structure is quite all right but its function is impaired.) Now the patient is a co-worker with the physician. The accent is not on "the counselor knows best" or the patient must "follow the doctor's orders," but on two people working together. It is understandably difficult for the doctor to assume this role. After all, his entire training prepared him to give of himself to the patient, not to ask the patient to take equal responsibility.

It is expecting quite a bit of the doctor to ask him to move easily between being an authority in a predominantly physical situation and being a "co-worker" when emotional problems are central. Such shifting of gears is necessary as the conversation moves back and forth between physical and emotional matters. It requires great flexibility in the physician, but a number of doctors seem able to make the adaptation called for. That is to say, the emotional and ethical state of the physican is of extreme importance in that his "self" is actively encountering the "self" of his patient. If there is a lack of flexibility on the physician's part, this will necessarily be communicated to the patient. The physician who wants his patient to be frank and open with him must create an atmosphere of trust and respect.

Because many people naturally find themselves consulting the doctor or the minister about a great number of problems, it is essential to guard against falling into unhealthy professional attitudes. With waiting rooms and studies becoming more and more crowded, we who are doctors or ministers are tempted to think we *are* authorities on numerous matters. As a result, we begin to treat people as if they were our children and we were their "all-knowing" fathers. In effect what we say is, "There, there; I'll tell you what to do." For a time such an attitude may keep some people from doing anything drastic, but this attitude will not help individuals face future situations alone. Of course, we receive a certain amount of satisfaction from manipulating the lives of others who are all too willing to let us take over making decisions for them. However, if we continually do this, it may actually be a sign of our own insecurity. As long as we play God to these people and their gratitude feeds our egos, we do not have to allow anyone to break through our outer shells and discover how really insecure we are underneath this authoritarian front.

Another attitude doctor and minister must be cautioned against is the feeling that everyone who walks into the office is in need of "psychological surgery." A professional person with such an attitude probes deeply into people's lives. Naturally the person will resist this treatment, but the professional man ignores this reaction for, after all, he feels he knows best. However, this very insensitivity to human feelings usually renders the professional man less able to help people.

Then there is the doctor or minister who diagnoses and labels the person's problem before knowing the whole story. He may do this either because he loves to talk and hates to listen, so he turns the person off as soon as possible; or because he finds that by putting people in set categories and treating those in each category the same way, he can see almost twice as many persons.

The goal of therapeutic conversations in the minister's study and in the doctor's office is to preserve a healthy balance between real authority based on expert knowledge, and the person's right to work through human problems in a free and empathetic relationship. The person must never be left without some responsibility, for if he knows that decisions will be made for him he will hesitate to exert himself as a co-worker in the process. The faculty of responsibility is strengthened by exercising it. While this may be a lengthier process in the beginning, its over-all effectiveness will be more enduring and thus less time-consuming. The advantage is that the person will have learned something about handling future difficulties by himself. It seems foolish to have to emphasize "proceeding at the other person's pace" because this factor is thoroughly realized in other areas of experience. However, the minister and the doctor are tempted, perhaps more than other professional persons, to throw their weight around and to lecture or to preach at individuals who are in no condition to act upon such advice.

The parent who helps his child with arithmetic knows that he would do the child no favor by giving him the answers. Rather, he should attempt to understand how much knowledge the child has of arithmetic and then proceed from this point. The parent can skip no problems, for if he does, the child's inability to comprehend a particular step will become evident in more complex problems. Professional men know this obvious point and we need not belabor it further. But then why is it that recent research in professional conversation, particularly that of ministers and doctors, reveals that these men persist in giving people answers without going through the laborious task of helping the patient to understand and to help himself? Perhaps we have failed to see ourselves in the role of teacher and have thought of ourselves chiefly as preachers and advisers.

CHAPTER 3

The Do's and Don't's of Helpful Conversation

What are the suggestions made by students of counseling which could apply to the conversations of doctors and ministers? They often begin by giving some helpful "don't's." I shall attempt to answer the natural question, "What *do* you do?" but first let me comment on the following list of "don't's."

1. *Don't give orders to the person.* This way of helping may bring about a temporary change, but to maintain the change requires active participation on the part of the patient.

2. *Don't exhort.* Here the counselor becomes something of an evangelist and works the patient up to the point of "signing the pledge." While there is some value in signing pledges, it requires a great deal of follow-up to internalize the external decision.

3. *Don't make suggestions—too quickly.* The counselor's status in the community means that for some persons what the doctor or minister suggests had better be done. Reassurance and encouragement usually accompany such suggestions. But when reassurance is given too soon, as it often is, the result is essentially repressive because the patient has not yet expressed the negative feelings he needs to release. This premature reassurance then covers over and denies the person's own deep feeling about his problem.

4. *Don't go to the other extreme of letting every patient rattle on unguided.* If catharsis means only a one-sided recital by the patient, then it can hardly be described as a counseling relationship. While frequently the person just needs to "talk it out," this should not imply that catharsis is sufficient in itself. If a person is encouraged to say more than he wants, catharsis can be extremely

harmful. Because a quiet professional man may be more coercive in his silence than he realizes, it often happens that the visitor tries to please him by telling all. However, this may not be the time to tell all.

5. *Don't give too much advice.* It is almost impossible not to give advice occasionally, and everyone does it. However, it is becoming clear—and there is much to learn from this—that a lot of advice goes unheeded. Certainly in some situations people are incapable of handling their problems by themselves, but human dignity demands they have some part in arriving at solutions.

While "don't's" are of value, there are also some important things to *do*:

1. *Give the person sufficient time to tell his story in his own way and without diversions and obstacles.* But suppose there are parish duties waiting or an outer office full of people; what then? If the doctor or minister feels that he would really like to help this person, he can demonstrate his willingness to do so by suggesting a return visit at a time when he can give this person his full attention.

2. *Listen not only to the facts given, but be aware of the feelings behind the facts.* This is, perhaps, the most significant insight students of counseling have received in understanding what goes on when two people engage in earnest conversation regarding a problem. Formerly it was thought that if the counselor got the facts straight, then he was on his way to a solution. Now he has learned that it is more important to be aware of the feelings behind the facts because people act on the basis of their "feeling" more than on the basis of their intellect.

3. *Try to put yourself in the visitor's place and look at the problem as he sees it, not as you see it.* At first this seems like a waste of time. As professional people our experience tells us that the reason this person has a problem is because he is looking at it from the wrong point of view. We are tempted to force him too quickly over to our perspective so that he will see how foolish he is to let the situation overwhelm him. But the analysis of professional conversations shows that it is precisely when we do this

that our helpfulness decreases. Even though we may be right, it has been discovered that a person can best be helped when he senses that the counselor is willing to listen to his point of view. There is no substitute for what has been variously described as "understanding," "empathy," or the ability to "feel with" the person.

4. *During natural pauses in the conversation, respond to the person by describing what you understand him to be saying.* As he pauses in telling his story to get your reactions, instead of asking him possibly diverting questions, try to sum up, in a sentence or two, what you consider to be the essence of what he has been saying. For instance, if he has been telling you in some detail about his wife's death, you may make the brief but meaningful comment, "You miss her very much." The emphasis must be on "you" and on "your" feelings rather than on the counselor and how *he* feels about it.

5. *A person is being helped the moment he senses that you are beginning to understand him.*

We must be willing to go down into the valley with another person so that he knows he is not all alone in his struggle. It is this frantic feeling of "aloneness" which paralyzes the normal strength of the person. Our task at the outset is to relieve the panic and thereby to aid the patient toward becoming himself again. No problem is ever quite so overwhelming once the person knows that another human is beginning to understand it with him, and, furthermore, that this other individual is willing to share some of the burden. Strength to face problems is inherently present in every normal person, but panic created by a sense of isolation often blocks this strength. In surgery the diseased tissue is removed to allow for normal functioning; so, too, in counseling, the factor blocking the normal strength must be removed. And we have discovered the impeding factor is often fear of facing the problem alone.

Now how do these five points apply in an actual situation where a problem is presented to a physician? I am basing the replies of the doctors on the kinds of answers I have received from a number of physicians who have participated in these "What would you say?" discussions.

> The patient is a forty-year-old married man with three children. He has been to see his doctor only once—a year prior to this interview. The patient complained of a backache and so the doctor gave him some medication. This time he presents the same complaint of backache. The doctor has seen him briefly and has prescribed the same pills he gave him a year ago. The conversation begins as the patient is about to leave the office.

> *Patient:* "Well, doctor, thanks for these pills for my backache. They sure helped me a year ago when I had this same problem. I hope they do the same for me this time. [Pause] I've been wondering whether you think I ought to keep this same job or not. I've been working in this architect's office for five years now, and I don't know whether sitting over the drawing board day after day is a good thing. Maybe that's what brings on these backaches."

What are some possible replies by physicians? In a classroom of doctors we presented the patient's statement and then asked them to write down immediately what they would have replied. Here are five typical replies.

> *Doctor A:* "Why don't you get another job? Find something you like better."

This doctor gives the first reaction that comes to his mind. It does not take into account the problem of finding another job, or moving the family, or seniority rating in the present firm. It clearly indicates that the doctor had not thought this through.

> *Doctor B:* "If I were you I would get some outside work. It is not good to be cooped up in an office."

This answer stresses the "I" rather than the "you." The doctor tells him how he looks at it without trying to put himself in the patient's place.

> *Doctor C:* "What does your wife think you should do?"

This reply put in question form is diverting, for if the patient is to answer he must go into some discussion concerning his wife's feelings. While this answer may eventually lead into something profitable, why jump from where the patient is to a discussion of his wife? The patient may get to it, but let him get there in his own way.

> *Doctor D:* "Have you talked to your boss about getting a different chair? I know a fellow whose back straightened around fine after he got a new chair."

This doctor has listened to the patient's complaints about his backaches and feels they may be due to working over a drawing board. And they may be. But also expressed by the patient, though not so overtly, were some feelings about his work in general which should be given a chance to come out into the open. It is so much simpler to deal with problems of this kind by getting a new chair, rather than a new attitude. It is also tempting to use the same solution for every patient with the same complaint. But because a new chair helped one patient does not necessarily mean it will help another.

> *Doctor E:* "You feel that your backaches are somehow related to your work."

This reply is what I mean when I say, "Express to the person what you understand him to be saying." The doctor tries to reflect what the patient has said in terms of his basic feelings about his job and about his backaches. The doctor does not try to get specific or analytic at this point. He merely expresses interest in this man and in anything he cares to discuss about the relationship between his job and his backaches. The doctor does not know where the conversation will lead. He is not making any snap diagnosis. A thousand and one combinations of physical and emotional aspects might be involved in this case, and it would certainly be foolish for the doctor to begin giving advice. Besides, the doctor knows it is important to let the patient tell his story his own way. Prying or prodding may overaccent aspects of the problem, which may not be as vital in this particular case as those the patient would bring out by himself. It is the patient who is ill, not the doctor. The patient has undoubtedly spent many hours thinking about his problem. If he is given a chance to express himself he might possibly come up with insights which when coupled with the physician's training and experience will constitute a team approach to the problem.

We shall now proceed with the patient's reply as he probably would have responded to the type of statements made by Doctor E.

> *Patient:* "At first I liked my job; I got along fine and the work at the drawing boards really did not bother me until I came in to see you a year or so ago. Then I began to feel all tired out when I came home at night. I would have to stretch out on the floor for an hour before I could feel relaxed enough to eat supper. But now I guess I'm back in the same rut and I'll have to take some more pills to get over this thing."
>
> *Doctor A:* "How many pills did you take a day?"

This doctor is probably trying to decide whether the pills he has now prescribed are going to be strong enough to handle the pain. He wants to be sure he understands the amount of the pain so that the patient gets adequate relief. This is necessary except the doctor must decide whether he is going to treat just the pain or the whole person.

> *Doctor B:* "Well, these pills that I gave you should hold you. You won't have any trouble now.

Doctor B has a number of people in the waiting room. Since the nurse has indicated that some of the people are quite restless, he resorts to reassurance based upon his knowledge of drugs. It is true the patient will not feel the pain if he takes these pills regularly. They will mask the pain and the deeper problems possibly connected with it. At least the fellow will be put off for a few weeks and by then there may be more time to talk with him. The doctor means well, but his practice is so large that he has to cut corners somewhere. Consequently, he misses an opportunity to deal with a functional illness in its early stages. A year from now, maybe five years from now, this man will come into the office with more serious complaints. Then the doctor will *have* to take more time with him, but it will be much harder to get to the root causes. Of course, then the symptoms will be clearer—so clear that hospitalization may be necessary.

> *Doctor C:* "Why do you think you started having backaches a year or so ago?"

This is a good question and indicates the doctor's willingness to take a look at some of the root causes. However, the patient hesitates with his answer for this is a difficult question. Then in order to keep the conversation going, the doctor begins to say what he thinks, even before knowing enough of this man's history. What is worse, the doctor may frighten the patient by implying that it is "all in his mind," and so the patient is afraid to go on with his story because he is sure the doctor will fail to understand the really important factors. Doctor C is "jumping the gun," and although he may have some accurate insights, the patient cannot take it when the counselor is too far ahead of him. The doctor must be willing to "proceed at the patient's rate" of insight, even though this may seem unnecessarily slow.

> *Doctor D:* "You'd better start taking a little more exercise. Do you play golf? Have you tried the new golf course?"

Here the doctor rebuffs the patient. At least he gives the impression that he is not interested in listening. He wants to get the patient's mind off all these morbid thoughts. Maybe this is the patient's trouble: he spends too much time thinking about these things. The doctor says to himself, "If I could show a personal interest in him, maybe that would help." And it would help provided such interest were shown in a sympathetic attempt to discover what is behind this man's words. If the doctor is not going to listen to the patient's worries and negative thoughts, who is? Besides, these things are not so terribly morbid. The patient is asking for the privilege of taking an inventory of himself with the aid of a professional person, whose life is dedicated to helping people in trouble. It might not require much effort on the physician's part to help this patient come to grips with the facts and feelings which have been showing up in physical symptoms. Perhaps no one has ever been willing to help him understand how the inner self takes out some of its unhappiness on the body. He has a right to ask, "Why does my doctor shy away from me when I try to express some of my deeper feelings? Is he bothered by them? Is this entirely outside his field? Where do I go from here? Will I need a psychiatrist? Am I really that bad?" No, he really is not in need of a psychiatrist. He could be helped tremendously by his doctor or his minister if either of these men would take the time to try to help him talk about himself and his work in relation to what he hopes to make of his life.

> *Doctor E:* "I see." [And he makes a gesture which encourages the man to continue.]

At this point this seems to be the best thing to do. Why interrupt or divert or advise when the doctor is just getting to know this man? Doctor E simply helps him to be at ease and to know that what he is saying is worth listening to. Such an attitude frequently encourages a patient who has previously been cut off in any attempt to express himself. The patient thinks, "Can this be true? Is the doctor really willing to listen to me? He seems to understand what I'm saying. If only I could talk to him for half an hour, maybe I'd begin to get hold of this thing that's bothering me."

> *Patient:* "When I first started working at this place it looked as if I had a good future laid out for me. Then I began to have some difficulties at home and I know this was reflected in my work. I was fairly productive, but I lost my creativeness and this is what you've got to have to get ahead in architecture. When I asked the boss why I had not got some of the promotions due me, he said I was too irritable at times and that I alienated customers. That's all he would say and I have never been able to really talk to him."

> *Doctor A:* "Let me give you some nerve pills. I think you need to be quieted down a bit."

I hope the doctor who wrote this reply was only fooling, for he is quite obviously overlooking the root of the problem.

Doctor B: "Well, I'm sure this is going to work out all right now. [rising.] Any time I can be of help, let me know."

But the man is trying to let the doctor know that things are not working out all right. It is apparent that Doctor B does not want to be tied down to a problem which he considers out of his field. This leads me to ask, Just what is his field? Perhaps this is the major question raised by this book. Both the minister and the doctor are today in a transition period. At the present moment it is impossible to write an accurate "job description" for either of them. All along the minister has thought himself responsible only for the spiritual needs of people and the doctor for the physical. But now these two neat categories have been exploded. Man cannot be understood or helped when treated as if he were but the sum of his parts. Something extremely vital is missing when an attempt is made only to reassemble the parts to bring about wholeness. To understand the whole the doctor must not only understand the parts, but also see the whole in all its relationships.

The doctor who says, "I have no business getting involved in this man's personal problems," is expressing the natural reaction of a professional man who is already overworked trying to keep abreast of the latest medical findings. The minister whose concept of the ministry has been tied up primarily with preaching has much the same reaction as the doctor. He says, "I have no business getting involved in the emotional problems of my parishioners." Already the minister is overwhelmed by administrative work in his church, and he feels that he cannot keep up with still another requirement of being a pastor.

Yet this raises more fundamental questions: Is the doctor or the minister accenting the physical or the administrative, thereby moving further and further away from man as an individual? Who then will be left to treat man as a unique creation sacred in the eyes of God? Will the doctor end up seeing him only as a physical body or the minister as an undifferentiated member of a group?

> *Doctor C:* "What kind of man is this boss of yours? He must be a strange kind of man if he is not even willing to talk things over with his employees."

And perhaps it is a strange kind of doctor who is not willing to talk things over with his patients. Stranger yet is the fact that, like the doctor, we can always pick out those faults in others that are just like our own. It is so much harder to see them in ourselves. In that way we unconsciously seek to draw attention away from our own faults by magnifying them in others. Thus whenever we catch ourselves criticizing the boss as in this case, we had better ask why we were so alert to this particular fault.

> *Doctor D:* "You'll have to work out your family problems all right. These things just take time, that's all. By the way, how many children do you have?"

This is called "accenting the positive" as a way out of a difficult situation. While positive thinking has its place, this does not happen to be the place. If the doctor is honest, he will have to admit that he really does not care too much about this man's family or how many children he has. This is a brush-off and the patient will not be long in catching on. The doctor might just as well have said, "Listen, mister, I'm not interested in your family problems. You came in with a medical problem and I fixed you up. Now beat it so I can get through with my office hours." Of course, he would not be that rude, but despite his words of encouragement he will most likely have discouraged the patient.

> *Doctor E:* "So you feel that the problem is part family and part job. And you are wondering whether you ought to take a serious look at both of them."

This doctor has shown willingness to go along with the patient and take a serious look. He did not need to say, "Would you like to talk to me about it?" because the patient was already doing so and the therapy had already begun. The helping process does not need to be formalized by saying, "Now we are doing it." Things *are* happening which lead toward growth and solution wherever there is warmth and understanding. Therapy does not begin when certain counseling "techniques" are employed. It *has* begun when human love is demonstrated by a willingness to listen and to be concerned. New evidence of nature's spontaneous surge toward health, maturity, and integration comes as a result of a relationship built upon mutual respect for the sacredness and the importance of the individual.

We, as doctors and ministers, expect others to treat us as in-dividuals with inherent dignity and the right to think and to act for ourselves. Does the person who comes to us with a problem get this feeling while he is with us? Or does he lose his self-respect and self-dignity when he enters our offices? If we believe that a person grows from within, then why do we keep trying to super-impose our ideas from the outside? Why not emphasize how much more we can do if we help him think his problems through? In this way he can learn how to help himself by calling upon inner strengths which, though available to one with faith and trust, are walled off by anxiety, fear, and self-centeredness. What-ever insights the patient gains will have to be experienced before they become a part of himself. He has a right to reject or accept what he wishes, and we should so relate ourselves to him that we do not interfere with those rights. He is not to be treated like a small child whose "father knows best." The professional helper does not always know best, and even if he did, he would only be manipulating the patient, not helping him toward self-under-standing.

How much freedom can the patient be given? Can we allow him to take issue with us? If we do not dare give him much free-dom, does this say something about ourselves; that we are not as convinced of our own position as we think we are? Do we really believe that new strength comes to a person because of, and through a deep relationship with, another human being who cares about him? Is this not what the Christian faith is trying to teach us; that God is present wherever love and concern for one's neighbor are to be found and that the healing and strength which become apparent are really God-given? It is nothing *we* give the patient. We only make its release possible because this gift flows so naturally through the channel of love and concern.

Physicians and ministers who are sensitive to people realize that just because a person says, "Yes, Doctor," or "Yes, Pastor," does not mean that he will follow the advice. A patient's very politeness and willingness to agree may mean that the sooner he can get away the better, for then he can continue to do exactly as he pleases. A person seldom tells his physician how many of his pills he has thrown into the wastebasket, nor does he tell his pastor how much of his advice was ignored because it was not wanted.

It is not the counselor's task to direct a person's life. Even if it were possible to be with the patient twenty-four hours a day and to make every decision for him, it would be an attack on the patient's right to grow in his own way. The counselor's task is to help the patient understand why he looks at life the way he does and to decide whether or not his philosophy is adequate. A little child who is learning to walk needs someone to catch him when he falls, or at least to provide something softer than cement on which to fall. But the child does not need to be carried from one chair to the other. If every time the child started walking, his parent carried him to the other side of the room, he would never learn how to walk. Why should we ministers and doctors try to carry our patients? We talk too much. Whenever the person begins to say something negative, we enter in with something positive so that we will not have to listen to what the person is really thinking down inside. Furthermore, we encourage the patient at a moment when we should be dealing realistically with discouragement, not glossing over it.

Growth toward maturity does not move on a straight line upward. If we recognize this then we can appreciate the actual contribution toward growth made by "down days" and negative feelings. Seward Hiltner has described growth in this way. A person goes along on a plateau for a while with nothing special happening to him. Then one day he comes up against something that is too difficult for him to handle and he drops down into a low mood. For a time all looks black and he sees no hope in struggling against his problem. When he finally hits bottom he is forced to do something about himself. Usually he does not do anything constructive until he is somewhat frightened by his predicament. Then there is a gradual thrust upward and forward as he learns something more about himself and conquers what he never thought he could. The thrust brings him to a slightly higher plane than he was on before. At this point he levels off on another plateau of living. Thus growth takes place in three directions: *dip, thrust,* and then *plateau.* When the person comes to the doctor or minister he is usually in the dip phase and has been frightened enough to want to do something about himself. It may be that he has not dipped as far as he will need to before he is willing to try the thrust upward. Our task in counseling may sometimes be to help him become more despondent and dissatisfied with himself so that eventually he will be determined to participate in reconstructing his way of facing his problems.

From this experience the doctor knows that sometimes matters have to be made worse before they can become better. If a patient has a sliver in his finger, the doctor tells him in a matter-of-fact way that before he can get the sliver out there will be some pain involved. We will frequently deal with people who have come to us for help because they feel some physical or spiritual pain. But when we get to know the person and see the problem has deeper roots, it is quite a temptation for both the patient and us to want to settle for mere symptomatic treatment. This is where accenting the positive may temporarily seem to bring about a quick cure. Yet most diseases of the whole man need to be dealt with at their source if any lasting help is to be given.

CHAPTER 4

Understanding the Person

If the person is the center of interest to the doctor and the minister then it will be profitable to look at some of the newer ways of describing how a person functions.

Suppose we begin by looking at man's mind. We have been taught that there is much more to our minds than appears on the surface. In our ordinary dealings with man we are aware only of his conscious mind which, we are told, is but an infinitesimal part of his entire mind. The unseen hopes, motives, memories, and frustrations lie deeply hidden in the "unconscious mind," which in turn is revealed in symbolic actions of which the psychologists have become increasingly aware.

Perhaps we can conceive of the mind as being analogous to an iceberg. We are indebted to psychiatry for this schematic concept of the iceberg. Of course we must remember that this illustration is only meant to suggest these newer ways of describing what goes on inside of us. Above the water line of this iceberg appears what we may call the conscious mind—a mere ice cube compared to the vast underwater portion which represents the unconscious mind. Formerly the unconscious was statically depicted as a musty old warehouse where past memories quietly rested on shelves until they were wanted. Then one opened the door and went down to aisle five on the third shelf and picked up the desired memory.

Today we believe that such a picture gives a very inadequate conception of how things operate on the unconscious level. Instead of visualizing a warehouse, we should think of a river into which a waterfall is rushing. The river consists of three general layers: the top layer, which is vigorously churning; the second layer, which is active but less violent; and the bottom layers which are gently flowing.

Applying this illustration to the lower portion of the iceberg, or to the unconscious mind, it might look something like this: Near the water line are those experiences and memories of the immediate past, say the last twenty-four to forty-eight hours. Like the churning water at the top of the river, these recent memories keep bubbling up into the conscious area—that small part which is above the water line. It is not difficult to recall something that happened yesterday, and if it is quite important, it keeps coming back to us again and again, influencing our present actions in a way which is clearly indicative of the impact of past experiences on present thoughts and actions. However, when we deal on a deeper level with experiences of many years ago, we assume that these memories are forgotten and no longer influence us. It is entirely feasible that we have forgotten them—on a conscious level, that is—but in light of our present understanding, these past memories continue to be active factors in the dynamic process.

We have only a sketchy idea of the workings of the unconscious, yet because of the growing evidence that past experiences *do* affect the present moment we cannot help but speculate about the interrelationship.

Experiences of the recent past—a year or two ago—are to be found in the second layer. These experiences and memories play an active part in the dynamic unconscious, and, although we are not so aware of them, it is thought that like the experience of the immediate past, they influence our thinking in any given moment.

In the third or lowest layer we find experiences that occurred in the distant past, even back to the time of birth. (Carl Jung would add that this layer also includes a "collective unconscious" which we have inherited from past generations.) This is by far the largest layer. While its dynamic, surging character is less noticeable than the obvious activity of the layers above, we should not think that these memories are shelved in a quiet old warehouse. Rather, they are very much alive and they do become evident when stimulated by the person himself at a time when his decision requires the insights of previous experience.

While we may think that decisions take place in the conscious mind, evidence seems to indicate that they are made at the meeting place of the conscious and the unconscious. Without our realizing it, some of these dynamic unconscious pressures push and shove their way into the area which might be described as the "area of decision-making." Decisions then are a combination of the external situation in consultation with a variety of inner drives with which we must daily reckon, even though we may be unaware of their existence. Another way to say it is that we cannot get away from ourselves and the experiences which have gone into the make-up of this vast and still mysterious unconscious.

In this book my interest in the unconscious is simply to stress that there is much more to man than appears on the surface. Any doctor or minister who would like to help a man in trouble had better get to know him on a deep level. This is why young clergymen are told not to rush in with counsel and advice until they have had a chance to consider thoughtfully what the person is saying. The clergyman may take everything a person says at face value, but there is a chance that this person might be saying exactly the opposite of what he deeply feels. Therefore, serious counseling requires time for relaxed conversation over a long period. If the person realizes that the counselor is not going to ride roughshod over him or make a quick analysis of his trouble, then he will feel less under pressure to "give us the facts." In such a leisurely atmosphere he will more likely reveal his true self by describing how he *feels* about this situation or that. It is essential that we be more aware of a man's feelings than the facts he expresses, for man is driven to action by his feelings, not by facts alone.

THE PROBLEM OF THE CONSCIENCE

I think it might be helpful to introduce a discussion of the conscience early in this book because doctors and ministers frequently report that parishioners and patients say they are confused about the meaning of the conscience.

To continue the iceberg illustration, let me say that at the water line or level of consciousness there is a trap door through which everything from the unconscious mind must pass before it can get to the conscious area. Standing at the door is a fellow whom I shall call the Conscience. The psychologist might call him the Super Ego or the Censor. As soon as he is described as the Censor, everything about him takes on negative connotations. Many people do equate the word "conscience" with something negative. They say it is something inside that tells a person what *not* to do. However, they forget that the Christian conception of the conscience includes the positive aspects as well, for it is also the instigator of the good if it is a well brought up, healthy conscience. The point is that consciences are of all sizes and shapes and they are important in either helping or hindering what the doctor or minister is trying to do for the person.

THE UNDERDEVELOPED CONSCIENCE

I will describe the two extremes of conscience and suggest that the average person has a conscience fitting somewhere in between. At one extreme is the small, underdeveloped conscience. I like to think of him as a very small man, smaller than the trap door of which he is supposed to be in charge. As the keeper of the door he is almost totally ineffective, for whenever pressures and expressions of feeling from the unconscious wish to get out, they do so by simply pushing open the door.

In order to illustrate an underdeveloped conscience, let us consider the case of a little boy, whom I will call Jack. At seven Jack was already the worst "problem child" in his grade school. Whenever he did not get his way he used profane language, kicked the teacher, and generally upset the whole class. The principal did all he could to help, but finally he sent the lad to the child guidance clinic. It was at the clinic that I learned of this boy's problem. The psychiatric social worker made a careful study of the boy in an effort to discover what went into this child's make-up. Her report was discouraging but believable. The boy lived with his mother in a one-room flat above a tavern. She had not wanted the child in the first place and she reminded him of this from time to time. Jack did not know who his father was. His mother made her living in devious ways and frequently the lad was literally kicked out of the apartment while his mother had one of her parties. As he roamed the streets alone at night, he developed such a tough exterior that even ten-year-olds were afraid of him. To the other children in his room Jack was a hero to be envied, for he seemed to be afraid of nothing and he could even talk back to adults.

However, the social worker made it clear that the closer she got to this boy, the more she became convinced of his loneliness and his fear. She said that he lacked two things vital to the development of a healthy conscience—love and discipline.

When I heard the social worker use the two words "love" and "discipline," it reminded me that the word "discipline" is derived from the word "disciple" and that a disciple is one who is willing to be disciplined by his leader or the master who loves the disciple in a mature and constructive way. This is one of Christianity's basic premises.

Or to state it another way, the entire contents of Scripture may be put in either of two categories, Law and Gospel, or to use our former words, Discipline and Love. In the seminary most pastors have been taught that every sermon ought to contain a balanced diet of love and law. If love is overaccented without balancing it with law, then love tends to deteriorate into a sentimental attitude and to lose its strength and structure.

To get back to seven-year-old Jack, it might be said that his conscience failed to develop because there was no one who cared enough about him to help him build one. Remember that when I use the word "discipline," I do not mean "punish." Punishment tends to have a destructive flavor, while discipline ought to connote constructive action. Someone might say that at least Jack was never repressed and, therefore, he did not develop the problems connected with repression. If we were to think of the conscience purely as a censor, then Jack might be thought to have some advantage in his freedom to say and to do what he pleased. However, the healthy conscience is always an encourager of the good. The real difficulty is that in any human society a person either has to have his own "built-in" controls or else society, through the police and the courts, will enforce some external controls on him. The conflict between the dynamic pressures of the unconscious and the requirements of society either takes place around the area of the trap door with the individual making his own decisions in a gradually maturing fashion, or else decision-making is taken away from him and placed in the hands of society. If, in the next few years, no one comes into Jack's life as a loving force, then the prognosis is very unfavorable. There is a good chance that he will end up in the courts where he will be described as a "psychopathic personality" or a "sociopathic personality." Those who have tried to work with children who have never known love or discipline realize the infinite patience needed to gain the confidence of these children and to help them channel their energies along constructive lines.

THE RIGID CONSCIENCE

At the other extreme of the two types of consciences is the *over*developed, rigid, and negativistic conscience. A person with such a conscience believes that everything is right or wrong, black or white. There is no flexibility and no sense of humor. In my illustration this conscience is a huge man who towers over the trap door. Dressed like a police officer, he carries a huge club. He looks very suspicious and threatening and spends most of his time holding the trap door down with his big foot.

An example of this negativistic or rigid conscience can be shown by another little boy of seven whom we shall call Fred. He lives in quite a different setting from Jack. He is one of four children born to a couple who have very high standards. They are determined that their children are going to be the best youngsters in the neighborhood. And they work much too hard at it. While they openly acknowledge love's power to mold a child into a good and useful citizen, these parents have more confidence in the law as a deterrent to wrong living. They carry this too far and so their discipline is actually more like punishment. Fred's parents withhold their love lest Fred interpret this love as a weakness on their part.

A typical day in Fred's life is a series of restrictions and "don't's." An example of this was an encounter between the boy and his father when the father accused Fred of doing something of which he was not guilty. As Fred tried to explain by saying, "But Daddy, I didn't . . ." his father immediately said, "Don't you 'but Daddy' me!" When Fred persisted, his father clamped his hand over the boy's mouth and sent him to bed without a chance to explain himself. Sleep did not come to Fred for hours because his insides were churning like the water at the foot of Niagara. He lay in bed unable to cry, unable to express himself in any way because he had long since learned that his father would punish him even for crying. Later when his mother asked where Fred was, his father replied, "Fred tried to talk back to me, but I put a stop to that and sent him to bed. No child of mine is going to go contrary to what I say."

In view of the foregoing comments concerning the dynamic nature of the unconscious, Fred's father only *thought* he had "put a stop to it." Actually all he had succeeded in doing was to slam Fred's "trap door" shut with his—the father's—big foot. Fred's true feelings were now all bottled up, trying to find expression. As a result of the inflexibility of his father, it was necessary for Fred to suffer in silence. When a child lives with a father or mother who requires him time and time again to respond in this way, it leaves a permanent mark on his personality structure. The unfortunate result is that Fred tends to identify himself with his father, even to the point of developing the same kind of rigid conscience. Children often are like their parents, even though they react with hostility to such parents. However, it is worth noting that each child reacts to his parents in his own particular way.

For instance, in Fred's family, the three other children are built differently psychologically. While the father often speaks in much the same way to the other children, they are able to stand up to him in way that Fred seems unable to do. Constitutionally Fred is meeker, less able to fight back, and therefore easier to control. Consequently, the father tends to be strictest with him. The other children get by with many more things than Fred does. Unfortunately, parents are inclined to be most rigid with children who are the easiest to manage and who seem unable to talk back.

What happens to a typical Fred as he grows older? The chances are that he will respond to other people having authority, such as teachers, scoutmasters, foremen, etc., in much the same way as he did to his father. Or, if he develops the ability to express contrary opinions to people in authority, it will be because he has become aware of this unnecessary repression and has fought hard to overcome it.

Physicians and ministers encounter far more people with over-rigid consciences than ones with the underdeveloped type. A general misconception is that people with overdeveloped consciences are overreligious, but rigidity can be found in people who have no connection whatsoever with religion. Their parents may just be the type who enforce extremely rigid standards on their children. Those who try to help such people must not get the impression that this is all bad, for a rigid conscience is far easier to modify than the opposite type. In trying to help the person with an underdeveloped conscience, it appears that there is nothing to work with and change because the concept of "I ought" or "I ought not" has never been developed. With the rigid conscience, there is a great deal to work with and the person himself is often aware of his own rigidity and will co-operate in trying to make some changes. A large percentage of the people who go to doctors and ministers with their troubles are those in the rigid category. They are people who have great difficulty releasing their bottled-up feelings in a wholesome, constructive manner and so they make themselves and those around them miserable.

CHAPTER 5

Ways of Releasing Tension

As ministers and doctors try to understand how to help people, it is essential that they recognize the many different ways individuals release tensions which build up in them. There are normal or constructive ways of handling tension which actually serve the good purpose of spurring people on to creative and worth-while activity. But there are also destructive ways of releasing tension which make people so ill that they concentrate on the symptoms of their sickness and thus often fail to get at the cause. In this chapter I will deal briefly with some ways of handling tension. I hope to make the point that tension is normal, but that it can be released either creatively or destructively.

Here are four of the many constructive ways of releasing tension:

1. *Talking it out.* All of us can remember times when we came home from work feeling that we could never go back to that job again. We were filled with resentment against our employer and everything connected with our work. We may have been too angry even to eat dinner. But as someone at home succeeded in drawing the story out of us and we could speak "feelingly" about it, our tension gradually diminished. Within a few hours we were viewing the situation much more objectively.

Much of this catharsis or talking it out is done in the natural give-and-take of discussions with family and friends. This is particularly true in communities where a good deal of neighborliness occurs. But in the isolation of city life, where the worker speaks to almost no one outside his own apartment, it is essential that there be someone in his family to whom he can talk. If he has no one to whom he can confide the daily hurts and insults of life, the pressure could build up inside to the point where it would have to find release in some sort of abnormal physical symptoms.

Doctors and ministers often see a patient or parishioner who is close to the breaking point and who at that very moment needs someone to listen to him or he will explode. As he pours out his story for an hour or two, the counselor finds that all he has to do is to show by the expression on his face that he is listening, and to respond with an occasional word of understanding. Ordinarily this person may not be the talkative type, and yet at this particular moment in his life he simply has to find someone whom he respects to hear him out. And an important point is that such people—people who are usually quite reserved—will not talk to just anyone. They will choose only someone in whom they have confidence: if they fail to find such a listener they will not talk at all. And if a person finds no one to talk with, he may develop physical or emotional symptoms.

Following an interview in which the doctor or minister has listened and said little or nothing, it very often happens that the patient or parishioner does not come in for several weeks and then returns only to express his gratitude to the listener for "doing so much for me when I was in trouble." The listener feels guilty for having done "absolutely nothing." Yet at the moment the person first came to him, there was a need for the empathetic spirit of one in whom he had confidence. Then having expressed his intense feelings he was able to regain his equilibrium and to handle his own problems.

Not everyone can handle his problems with such dispatch. Yet most people cope with their daily smaller problems in a variety of conversational settings. It is only occasionally that there is a need to talk with a professional person, and then only because the problem does not respond to the usual "talking it out" with family and friends. However, our churches would do well to make it easier for people to feel free to talk with the minister about any matter so that they would not hesitate as they now do. If "talking it out" is potentially an opportunity for creative discussion, then it ought to be encouraged as a part of the pastoral care available to everyone.

2. *Recreation, which may include physical activity.* In the course of a day we ought to change our type of activity from time to time. Most of us can work at one thing only so long, and then we need to change our pace. Even though we all know this, the pace of our present world is such that we often fail to realize that recreation is absolutely essential for every one of us. As a result we fail to see how re-creative such daily experiences can be. Of course there are some people who are as taut on the golf course as they are at the office, and they hold the golf club with the same intensity as they do the pencil. For a person to get the most value from recreation he must have an attitude of mind which permits the gears to be shifted into neutral. People who are most gifted with the ability to change pace say that even the most rigorous physical chores around the house serve them well as a form of recreation. Recreation then is understood as giving balance to life as well as relief from tension. It gives us an opportunity to stretch ourselves in other directions.

3. *Being able to laugh and cry—in proper proportions.* People with a good sense of humor are fortunate indeed. Healthy humor implies the ability not merely to tell funny stories, but to be able to look with humor *at oneself* when the going is rough. This is quite different from the person who must be the life of the party and always has to be making clever remarks—perhaps because he cannot face himself.

Tears are closely related to humor. Crying too is an excellent way to release inner tension. But in our society men in particular have been taught from childhood that it is weak to cry. It frequently happens that a man will come to the pastor or doctor with a very tense expression on his face. We may begin to converse with him, and he answers in monosyllables as he attempts to control his emotions. Then suddenly, as the conversation moves into a tender area, he breaks down completely and his sobbing is almost uncontrollable. He has a look of fright or even terror as he blurts out between sobs that he knows he is "done for now" because he has let his emotions get out of control. He feels he is on his way to a nervous breakdown or even insanity. But even as he is able to admit this his tenseness decreases and he seems to relax and sit more naturally in the chair. Then as a new calmness takes over we can remind him how important it is for men as well as women to have a good cry when the pressure builds up to a point where it cannot be handled in the usual way.

Tears are usually the last thing a man will allow himself. He has battled his way through life this far without tears and he is determined to continue to do so. Often it takes a good deal of persuasion to convince him that crying may be the healthiest thing he can do; that a healthy cry can be the safety valve which temporarily takes care of the intense pressure within and gives him the opportunity to talk about his problems in a way that he could not prior to the emotional release. For some reason in our Christian culture we give people the impression that a good Christian does not give in to weeping. Despite the fact that "Jesus wept" on several occasions, we persist in creating the picture of a Christian as one who always has everything under control. In other words, if a person is "really right with God" he would not need to cry. Certainly Jesus was right with God, and yet even he found tears necessary and normal in certain times of stress.

As important as it is to be able to laugh and to accent affirmations of faith and hope and trust, it is equally important for a person to be able to express his feelings of discouragement and defeat when these are present. To refuse to admit that one has such negative feelings from time to time is only to repress them and thereby to cause their dynamic power to come out in some very undesirable, abnormal manner.

4. *To open one's inner self to God through prayer and worship.* Prayer comes just as naturally to man as talking things out, or recreation, or humor, or tears. But many people have not been

helped to see how natural prayer is. Or they use it only in moments of crisis because praying is a native tendency. But in such
moments of crisis prayer is not nearly so helpful as it could be
had these people learned to pray during happier times. Harry
Emerson Fosdick in his remarkable book *The Meaning of Prayer**
says, "Praying is a practice like breathing or eating . . . men
engage in it because they are human, and *afterward* argue about
it as best they can. . . . Somewhere in every man there is the
capacity for worship and prayer, for the apprehension of God
and the love of him. Is not this the distinctive quality of man and
the noblest faculty which he possesses?"

The word "worship" has been included in this fourth way of
releasing tension to emphasize that man comes into contact with
God not only in his solitude through prayer, but also in fellowship with other men in the gathering together for common worship. In this worship experience each of us is reminded that our
relationship to God is by no means limited to times when we
cry out to Him for help. Worship reminds us that God desires
to be in constant communion with us, and if such a close relationship is broken it is we who have strayed from Him, not He
from us. In the moments of meditation accompanying worship
we often come to see how we separate ourselves from God to our
own destruction. The hope is that we will then desire to return
to Him. The way by which one returns to God has been described
by Christians throughout the centuries as the *Way of Salvation*.
Because the word "salvation" means healing or wholeness it
could also be described as the *Way of Healing*. Throughout the
centuries Christians have taught this way of salvation to their
children in the hope that each new generation's faith might be
revitalized. Today the validity of this way of salvation has been
attested psychologically, for it shows a remarkable understanding of the nature of man. It not only sees man as he is but also
points to what he needs in order to be freed from the fetters
which bind him—the fetters which keep him from being a fully-
functioning, integrated, mature human being.

* New York: Association Press, 1949.

In this generation the churches may have failed to make this way of salvation explicit enough. In its briefest form it might be expressed in six statements, all of which are predicated upon the belief that God initiates this relationship to which man responds.

1. *We become aware of our separation or alienation from God.* Something in our life forces us to realize our self-inadequacy and shows us our need to be in relation to a power greater than ourselves.

2. *We are made conscious of our personal part in bringing about this situation of alienation.* We recognize that this emptiness of our life is our doing, not God's.

3. *We confess our sinfulness as we repent of our self-centeredness, pride, and willfulness.*

4. *We receive God's forgiveness* as declared through His promise in Scripture.

5. *We become a new person.* (Our sense of isolation is gone.) This is not to say our problems are taken from us, but we are no longer alone in facing them.

6. *Out of gratitude to God we now desire to do His will.* Our good works come, then, as a result of what God has first done for us and not the other way around.

This Way of Salvation is not a once-in-a-lifetime experience. Because of our human weakness we constantly separate ourselves from God and constantly need re-established relationship with him.

Gratitude plays a most important part in the Christian's discovery of salvation. Out of gratitude for this sense of oneness with God the person now seeks to serve God with his whole being. There is something in this unique feeling of relationship to God which calls out in a man a new quality of motivation. This remarkable force should be made available to every person a minister attempts to help. If we fail to help a person realize that such a way is open to him, it would be as if a physician withheld a life-saving drug from his patient. No true release of tension is possible for a man until he has clarified his own relation to God through prayer and worship. In talking things out with God in prayer or through confession to a fellow human who represents this "power not of ourselves," there comes a most amazing knowledge of having been heard, understood, forgiven, and accepted although unacceptable. It is this experience which ultimately is needed if man is to be truly healed.

What about the abnormal or destructive ways of releasing tension? The case of Fred (see Chapter 4) presents a person who has never been able to talk, to relax through physical activity or recreation, to laugh or cry about his problems. Moreover, his religion only reinforced his rigid conscience. Here is one who is sick and needs help. The pressure in the lower part of the iceberg has been building up because he has kept the trap door shut so long that the normal channels of release are not available to him. But the pressure has to go somewhere. As it begins to press against the "walls" of the total person it is trying to find a weak spot. If the pressure cannot get out through the normal channels it has to resort to abnormal ways. The physician is often the first to see pressure being released through such common abnormal channels as the following. (We are obviously not speaking about all patients but rather about those whose illness is primarily functional. This group is described by various physicians as including from 40 to 60 per cent of their patients.)

1. *"Nervousness"* (to use the common name). Parish ministers have to work with more than their share of "nervous" people. A parishioner says, "Pastor, I've been so nervous lately. The doctor says it's my nerves, so I'll have to slow down. That's why you won't see me at Guild meetings for a while."

The pastor does not press the issue but he is bothered by the naïve conception which otherwise intelligent people have concerning nerves. They prefer to think that something is wrong with their neurons and ganglia and that the doctor is putting these back in good repair. It is like saying, "I have a broken leg." As long as a patient can point to a physical something supposedly injured or sick "outside" his inner self, he feels he does not have to apologize for it. The doctor knows this and has gone along with it. So has the minister. It might be helpful occasionally, however, to confront the patient with a more accurate description of what the doctor means by "nerves."

Why should the patient, who could do something constructive about the cause of his "nerves," be kept from doing it because the doctor does not want to upset him or insult him? We can sympathize with the doctor who says, "I can tell a patient that he has 'neurasthenia' [weak nerves] and he is perfectly willing to accept this diagnosis. But it is quite a different thing to tell him that he has 'psychasthenia,' for he would translate this as meaning a 'weak mind.'" But if "psyche" could be given its original meaning, "soul" or "spirit," then we could help the patient understand that it is his spirit that is weak, that he needs some help in strengthening his outlook on life.

It is unfortunate that some illnesses which are essentially brought on by spiritual insecurity are treated only with tranquilizers that lull the patient into a false sense of security. Doctors' offices are crowded with people who are trying to run away from facing up to themselves. Naturally everyone prefers to think there is nothing wrong on the inside—that it is purely a mechanical problem which a doctor can fix. Perhaps doctors are needed who will say to certain patients, "There is nothing wrong with your nerves; but there is something wrong in your living. When you are ready to take a self-inventory, I'll be glad to help you."

2. *The skin.* There has been a great deal of debate about the degree to which the skin mirrors what is going on inside. But certainly the skin is one of the first parts of the body to respond to what the person is feeling and thinking. The patient who comes to the family physician with a dermatological problem may in effect be saying, "Doctor, I have a skin problem, but I think there is more to it than that. Could you please help me with some of these other things too?"

This might well be the place to point out that there are dangers involved in getting too enthusiastic about the psychosomatic interpretation of illness. Certainly it is essential that the patient be adequately cared for somatically, but there is no cause for alarm about the present accent on the psyche because the basic scientific spirit of medical research will see to it that the soma is not overlooked. And further, from the present writer's point of view, the spiritual needs of patients have been ignored for so long that a few new books with this emphasis will not upset the balance of good medical practice.

3. *The gastrointestinal system.* This system of the body is perhaps the best known of all for its psychosomatic interrelationships. For over a hundred years medical literature has from time to time called attention to the frequency with which gastrointestinal disturbances can be seen in relation to emotional disturbances. William Brinton, a physician writing in 1858, maintained that in view of the frequency of this coincidence, mental anxiety should be regarded as a "more or less immediate cause" of ulcers. Another physician, Walter B. Cannon, writing in 1909 said: "An emotional disturbance affecting the alimentary canal is capable of starting a vicious cycle." He concluded therefore that "discomfort and mental discord may be fundamental to disturbed digestion." And since Cannon's time a great deal of research has been going on to demonstrate the relationship between the psyche and disfunction of the gastrointestinal system. The minister finds himself thinking about his parishioner Mr. Jones who has for years been troubled with an ulcer. He wonders, "Perhaps I should try to help Mr. Jones see how he is looking at life. Perhaps he would like some help in getting a better understanding of how life can be better for him."

4. *The cardiovascular system.* Any problem related to the heart is particularly upsetting, for of all the organs it is the one most prominently associated with keeping life going. If the heart is not functioning, then nothing functions. We talk about the heart in our everyday speech as the seat of human emotions. We say, for example, that a certain person is "heartless" while another is "warmhearted" and still another has a "heart of gold." Although it is not literally true that the heart is the seat of human emotions, it is true that the heart is very important in people's thinking about themselves. They consider it the source of their "spiritual"

as well as of their "physical" life. Thus people tend to focus a great deal of emotion on the heart, and this organ often becomes the recipient and expressant of much of a person's tension, worry, and anxiety. As Walter Alvarez, emeritus professor of medicine at the Mayo Clinic, comments, "We often say a person dies of a broken heart or of a heart attack. Hence just let a man get a pain in what he thinks is his heart, let him feel a missed beat, let his heart race for a minute, or let him feel a little harmless air-hunger, and he may instantly become a badly frightened man." Since the heart is the center of so much emotion, feelings come to exert a strong influence upon its functioning.

5. *The respiratory system.* Here we have the tantalizing problems of many allergies, especially asthma, hay fever, and the common cold. Like the other incapacitating illnesses, respiratory diseases represent the first line of defense and respond immediately to any disturbance in homeostasis be it shock or a stress situation. Helen Flanders Dunbar in her book *Psychiatry in the Medical Specialties** says, "The cold habit may be called a somatic reaction to frustration, irritation or a sense of injustice or neglect. . . . Susceptibility to pneumonia differs very little psychodynamically from susceptibility to colds." Dunbar goes on to comment about allergies in general by saying that "as a rule, allergies represent a kind of dramatic side show in the general adaptation syndrome. Allergies could almost be thought of as side reactions of the sudden shifts of body chemistry which occur when the organism is suddenly compelled to compensate under stress." Allergic disease then may be the body's way of expressing the person's reactions to unresolved life situations. It is true too that nervousness and fatigue or inability to cope with some inner problem can set the allergic trigger so fine that it can almost go off by itself. The allergist has to be extremely sensitive to the disturbances of the inner self, and if he is to be of real help to his patients he must be sensitive not only to what might be called

* Dunbar, Helen Flanders, *Psychiatry in the Medical Specialties* (New York: McGraw-Hill Book Company, 1959), p. 239.

purely psychological problems but also to the spiritual dimensions of such problems.

Why is it that in some people the pressure of tension chooses to come out in the form of a gastrointestinal complaint, while in others it takes the form of a cardiovascular symptom, and in still others it takes the form of a skin disorder? The answer seems to be simply that physiologically each of us is vulnerable at a different spot and so the weakest part of us yields to the pressure first. If the system "chosen" is not able to drain off the pressure by itself, a second and even a third system is employed.

The clergyman's interest in the psychosomatic approach to illness is based upon his concern that man must always be dealt with in his totality. The minister cannot help but encourage any approach that comes at problems wholistically. He knows that every doctor who converses with his patients, no matter how specialized the training and practice of the doctor may be, moves toward ministering to the whole man. When the physician is in his office talking with patients he is not simply a scientist. He is a human being influencing and being influenced by one of his fellows in one of the most wonderful experiences granted to us, that of the human relationship.

CHAPTER 6

The Psychosomatic or "Spiritbody" Approach to Health

One way to describe the close interrelation of body and spirit is to say that the body is a person's closest friend. The clergyman is especially interested in how medical people use the term "psychosomatic" because as a seminarian he frequently came across the word "psyche" in his study of New Testament Greek. The man in the street generally translates the word "psyche" as "mind" or "brain" as in Psychology—the study of the *mind;* and in Psychiatry—the healing of the *mind.* Here the connotation of the word "psyche" is clearly more physical than spiritual. Yet in the Greek, the first meaning of psyche is not mind or brain; it is "soul." Its second meaning is "spirit," or "breath of life." "Mind" would be a third definition, but this word in its usual sense excludes the spiritual aspects of man's being. "Somatic," the latter part of the word "psychosomatic," is derived from the word "soma" which is adequately translated "body."

Therefore, the clergyman hopes that any approach to illness which purports to be true to the basic meaning of the word "psychosomatic" will be cognizant of the full dimensions of the word. In its deepest sense, then, the word implies a wholistic or "spiritbody" approach to illness.

We began by calling the body man's closest friend. The relationship can be seen very clearly when we think of the sensation of pain when we step on a nail or get our finger too close to the fire. In such a situation, it is not difficult to understand the close relationship of body and spirit, or soma and psyche. A person is even grateful for the sensation of pain which abruptly tells him that all is not well with his body.

Now we are beginning to understand that the body, as man's closest friend, often tries to tell him when things are not going well with his *inner self*. It is as if he is stepping on "inner nails" which cause his body to call for help. Could it be that the doctor is seeing hundreds of people in his office who are actually in spiritual distress but who have not done anything about it until the distress finally expressed itself in physical symptoms? The doctor obviously would prefer to get to the cause of the problems which are presented to him. This is one of the real reasons why ministers and doctors ought to develop a close working relationship. If it is true that a large proportion of the physician's patients are basically suffering from spiritual distress, why not track the symptoms down to their real source?

If ever a team approach is required in helping people it is in unraveling the psychophysical problems of functional illness. The minister would like to participate in it because religion, after all, is concerned with man's attitude toward *all* of life, not with some little segment of it which some people would label the "religious." When a person accepts the Christian Way then it ought to color every aspect of his life, including the physical. Christianity is concerned about the body and never speaks of a person's spiritual nature as being unrelated to flesh and blood. As a "down-to-earth religion," the Christian faith sees man's spiritual problems always in the context of his day-to-day existence in a real world with a body to feed, a job to perform, and someone to care for. And in this real world the Christian faith is aware of all kinds of problems which estrange man from a close fellowship both with God and with his neighbor. Some of these are described as self-centeredness, materialism, envy, pride, hatred, and lust. On the other side of the picture are those attitudes which draw man closer to God and neighbor, such as love, joy, faith, hope, sacrifice, humility, and patience.

The person with functional illness needs help in facing a real world in a body which for some reason is rebelling. It is his task to try to understand what these bodily symptoms are trying to say to him. What is there about life which this person is unable to face? He is only "half living."

Let us go back to Fred. He is now about thirty years old. He has been thinking about seeing a doctor because he has so many diffuse symptoms of physical distress. He is still in the fetters of an overdeveloped, rigid conscience. He has never been able to find anyone to whom he can talk about his problems and so he has had no help in understanding why he has such a difficult time getting along with himself and others in this real world. To recall the iceberg illustration, we might say that there is a civil war going on in Fred near the water line. It is primarily because the trap door has been held down so long that the pressure which has been building up down below simply has to go somewhere. Because Fred is unable to use the normal channels for releasing tensions, they are now coming out in physical symptoms, which constitute the body's abnormal way of releasing tension in an effort to call attention to disturbances in the inner self.

Fred is one of these people who are only "half living." He does not enjoy life at all. He is only existing. This is also descriptive of Fred's religious life (as it is of so many people with functional illness). Fred neither enjoys his religion nor benefits from it. His conception of God is remarkably similar to his conception of his own father—legalistic, demanding, and authoritarian. Although Fred goes through the motions of prayer, he is unable to express his negative feelings to anyone, even to God. In his prayers, Fred says only nice things because he believes that God is not interested in his deep feelings. Furthermore, Fred speaks politely to God, just as he does to everybody, because this is the way to get along with people. He does not know what a truly human dialogue is, so of course he cannot be expected to participate in the divine-human dialogue. This is precisely the kind of mere existence which Christ spoke out against. It is evident that when a man only partially exists even his body cries out in physical symptoms which seem to be saying that man was made for more than this.

To be sure, when Fred comes to the doctor's office he has physical symptoms, but these are tied up tightly with the spiritual symptoms of nonfulfillment. Perhaps before the physician starts working on the physical problems he will want Fred to consider the possibility that his body may be frantically trying to call his attention to the needs of his inner self. This is where the clergyman comes in. However, it is hoped that there will be an increasing number of doctors who will develop the ability to explain this spiritbody relationship in such a way that patients cannot help but see the need for a two-pronged attack upon the presenting problems.

In some cases the patient may hesitate for a while to bring a minister into the situation and the physician will have to be both doctor and minister, as many have been in the past. Looking at it from one point of view, this might well be the goal of the best medical care. That is, the Christian doctor ought never compartmentalize the care of patients into physical and spiritual—with the minister handling the latter. To be sure, in many complicated situations the patient would benefit from the help of both the doctor and the minister. But this is not possible in all cases and so the doctor will use his years of religious education and training as a member of a church to give a spiritual ministry along with the physical. The ideal of the Christian community is not that the minister will give all the spiritual care, but that he will train all his people to give such care to others. He could not possibly minister to all the people who need it. This is why every Christian is called a "priest" in the doctrine of the "priesthood of all believers." Of all church members the physician probably has the greatest opportunity to share his faith and to minister to people in spiritual distress.

"Spiritual therapy" will begin for Fred as soon as he feels that someone is sincerely interested in his innermost feelings. Fred needs to talk with someone who will help him to say the things he finds so difficult to express. It will come as a pleasant surprise to him to learn that not all people who hold positions of importance act in an authoritarian fashion. As the doctor creates a warm and unhurried atmosphere Fred will begin to "take his first steps" in self-expression. The doctor can then invite him back a week later for another talk. After two or three of these talks in which the doctor has quietly pointed out emotional and spiritual overtones of Fred's problem, the doctor might recommend that Fred see "a minister friend of mine who understands people."

If such joint co-operation does result, Fred's relation to the minister should move in the following directions:

1. The minister and the doctor both help Fred to see Christian love and understanding in action, for they both accept Fred just as he is. Certainly they do not support Fred's concept of a tyrannical, authoritarian God and so Fred is forced to re-examine his ideas about God.

2. Fred's estrangement seems to be a result of his "partial existence." Gradually Fred should be helped to see that although his harmful attitudes toward people and his religion have been preconditioned by his early home life, yet he himself has to assume most of the responsibility for his present dilemma. The doctor, who may in this case be a psychiatrist, and the minister both help Fred to discover and correct some of the psychic defenses behind which he is hiding. In this way Fred becomes psychologically freed and thus able to search within himself for the sources of his problem.

3. Fred now realizes his own part in not actualizing his God-given potential to be a man in the fullest sense of the word. When he finds that the doctor and the pastor can and do accept him, he then wants to know more about this attitude of acceptance and mercy which he has overlooked in the Scriptures. This leads naturally to a restudy of the life and teachings of Christ and a new comprehension of the forgiving spirit Christ evidenced in all his relations with men. Christ had always been just a name to Fred. He had never tried to develop what Christians call "a living relationship" with him. As Fred becomes

better acquainted with Christ through the Scriptures, through conversations with other Christians, and through prayer, contemplation, and worship, he becomes more certain that he can have the same kind of open and honest relationship with God as he had experienced with the doctor and the minister.

4. Now Fred begins to mature as a Christian, and his way of praying shows it. Prayer becomes a real encounter with God at the beginning or the close of day as he wrestles to clarify the issues which confront him. He says exactly what he feels and he holds nothing back from God. The door to the unconscious is no longer clamped shut by a vague threatening force. He is on good speaking terms with his conscience. When the door needs to be closed against some harmful thought he does it quite consciously with full knowledge that he is controlling a drive which needs to be kept in its place. He is now able to handle the dynamic power of the unconscious in a manner leading to fulfillment, not to destruction.

5. Worship at its best becomes an opportunity for growth, for Fred sees that it calls upon man to examine himself honestly, and to admit, in the presence of God, what he finds in himself that is contrary to the will of God. This is known as "confession"; every service of worship should begin with it. Of course, it is essential that before a person begins such a confession, he must have a genuine sense of regret for those actions and thoughts which he knows are not only unhealthy, but also disobedient to what he recognizes as right and just and good. There must follow a sincere desire to change; a genuine conviction that a continuation of such wrongdoing and thinking will bring about estrangement not only from God but from his fellow men as well. This leads us to ask further questions concerning the nature of pastoral care.

PART II

How the Minister Functions in the Sickroom

PART II

*How the Minister Functions
in the Sickroom*

PART II

How the Minister Functions
in the Sickroom

CHAPTER 7

Aspects of Pastoral Care

Pastoral care is that part of the clergyman's task in which he seeks to give strength and guidance as he ministers, particularly to people who are going through periods of stress and anxiety.

Most professional counselors see their patients in the office of a downtown building. The minister, on the other hand, is usually able to talk with his parishioners in a more relaxed and natural setting, in a home or in his church study. Although a parishioner can be at ease in his home, young children or other members of the family may make it difficult to talk. For this reason the minister invites most people to talk with him in his church study. After the conversation the person can pause in the quiet of the church building to meditate—a lost art in this day. In the church the very atmosphere can help him to realize that he is not alone in his search for truth and self-understanding. Millions before him have found strength in prayer, meditation, in the Scriptures, and in hymns. As the person reads selections from the Scriptures or hymns they take on more meaning for him than usual. He realizes, for instance, in this moment of need that the hymns are not just meaningless poetry set to melody. Many of them are the fervent expressions of people who were going through moments of darkness similar to his own and who found their way with the help of God. The person may even begin to see that his period of turmoil can help him to grow toward maturity. When he was not faced with difficulties, it was easy to drift into a smug complacency, but when he is experiencing pain and suffering, he is compelled to search for the causes of his problems and for the real meaning of life.

Intensive concentration on the person's problem during the counseling hour and the private meditation of the individual which follows are important factors in working out a person's difficulty. But if a person thinks of therapy primarily in terms of talking, talking, talking—about himself—there is danger that this self-centeredness of the counseling hour may carry over into the other hours of the day. Furthermore, if intensive counseling is prolonged, this preoccupation with self cannot help but have harmful consequences. For instance, a doctor will use a powerful drug for a short period of time in order to get the patient's body chemistry back into balance. But this drug can be harmful if it is used so much that it takes over the body's job of keeping the systems functioning smoothly. Intensive counseling is likewise an "extreme" measure necessary for a short period of time, but it is never meant to hinder resumption of the normal activities of life. For the average person with a not too severe problem, this self-analysis could even unnecessarily arouse "sleeping dogs" which the person will probably never get around to handling anyway.

Counseling, then, must be balanced with other forms of help. And whenever possible, the person ought to continue to be involved in the life of the community. What the person does after working hours and between interviews is of extreme importance. Is he applying the insights of the counseling hour in his activities and relationships? Is he making a sincere and active effort to understand and to work through his difficulty?

The minister who wants to give more than counseling to people who come to him for help uses what may be termed the "between interviews" program. The minister still gives his complete attention to the person during the counseling period, but when the person seems able, the minister encourages him to give something of himself in the service of another individual, the community, or the church. This may take the form of calling on a shut-in or an elderly couple, or participating in a project sponsored by community or church. In this way the person is helped to keep from dwelling abnormally on his own problems. It also enables him to see that he cannot expect others to take an interest in his problem if he is unwilling to give something of himself for them.

The pastor has learned he can be of little help to a person who is unwilling to go out of his way for someone else, for then counseling may actually contribute to further egocentricity. The pastor who uses the "between interviews" program finds that it works wonders in clearing the docket of chronic complainers who really do not want to change and will not exert the effort necessary to do so.

It has been observed that people who are being counseled by the pastor have shown such an interest in this "between interviews" approach that they have been known to spend many hours giving volunteer service to hospitals, churches, and social agencies. These people want to change, and they are taking specific steps in this direction. Part of their counseling hour will perhaps be concerned with understanding their past in the light of present upsetting experiences. However, another part of the session will be devoted to the person's plans for the next hour and the next days and even weeks. Gradually the person's confidence in his ability to get well will increase as he sees himself able, right now, to break some of the small bonds which have made growth toward maturity so difficult for him. The experienced pastoral counselor does not force his parishioner to take a forward step before he is ready, but it is a good thing when the parishioner can try new ways of facing daily problems in a situation where he will feel little self-consciousness. Clearly no therapist, religious or secular, relies entirely on what happens in the consulting room.

Pastors have discovered that parishioners often appreciate an "assignment" which they are to complete by the time of the next interview. The assignment may be to read a brief chapter of a book which speaks to the kinds of problems presented. Or it may be that the person will be asked to outline the chapter or to write out a few questions which have occurred to him in the course of the reading. Usually it is far better to assign a short specific portion of a book rather than to say "Here's a good book I'd like you to read." And before giving it, the pastor should show some real enthusiasm for the book or at least explicitly point out reasons why he is giving this particular "prescription." It is entirely possible that the person may not be as struck by a chapter as was the pastor and after reading it may go on to another which he reports on with enthusiasm. The value of assigning reading is that it helps to keep the continuity of the counseling session, for even as the person reads the assignment he is reminded of certain points which were discussed with the pastor, and some of the ideas which had seemed of little value previously may now come alive in this setting.

There is always the possibility that the pastor, in his desire to avoid being dogmatic with individuals who come to him, will go to the other extreme and provide no structure whatsoever so that the person feels no sense of direction. Pastoral care can best be given within the framework of some kind of ordered discipline. The person who has come for help is usually willing to do almost anything to regain his "health." Of course if the minister's own life is not well-disciplined he probably will not see the value of suggesting discipline to someone else. Yet he must understand that when a person is going through a period of anxiety, he needs something specific to hold on to even more than he usually would.

In addition to reading it might be well to prescribe for the person a planned program of prayer and meditation involving perhaps five to fifteen minutes daily. The person in distress needs a kind of spiritual discipline to give him "personal" strength just as the athlete in training requires physical discipline to give him physical strength. It is often valuable to suggest that a person visit a church which is open daily for meditation and prayer. This provides something tangible for him to do, and sometimes proves to be particularly valuable for the office worker. Having to plan his noon hour so that he can find a five-minute period in a nearby church may help to break up certain other habit patterns which had been harmful to him. If the counseling the person is receiving is to have the effect of breaking bad habit patterns and beginning new ones, then it is essential that the new habits be carried on every day while the once-a-week conversations with the pastor help to reinforce these new patterns of thinking and conduct.

Nor should the parishioner be limited to being helped only by his pastor. It is entirely possible that other resource people in the community can combine their efforts with the pastor's in assisting a person during the difficult period of changing to a new way of life. This other help might well include regular attention from the family doctor, conversations with a psychologist or social worker, discussions with a family counselor—along with a new membership at the local YMCA, YWCA, or health club where he can participate in group athletics or social events. He might even attend a group discussion session where emphasis is given to understanding oneself in the presence of others.

The person being counseled by the pastor might also use the "between interviews" period to write up some notes about his own reactions to people and events during the week and thus try to analyze why he acts as he does. Further, he could describe ways by which he is attempting to develop more openness with persons with whom he has found it difficult to get along.

Thus far we have seen that the pastoral care program includes two major functions—the counseling hour and opportunities between interviews for the person to strengthen himself. However, a third aspect of the minister's program is made possible by the resources of the church itself. It is remarkable how many church members are asking for suggestions of ways they can demonstrate their faith by being helpful to people going through crisis experiences. Now that the counseling ministry is receiving so much attention, people have seen that they can assist the pastor in very tangible ways. For instance, a woman who is an interior decorator may be able to interest a "patient" in this work. Or another member of the church may help a "patient" become an amateur carpenter by spending evenings with him in his own basement workshop. In these ways a "patient" is given an opportunity to grow in many directions and to discover areas in which he may use his talents in constructive and productive ways. It has been found that if this type of "between interviews" treatment is combined with the other types of pastoral care, quite a bit can be accomplished in a one- to three-month period.

At this point it is well to insert the cautions of a psychiatrist who often reminds me that the natural and understandable impulse of the pastor is to emphasize to his counselee the resources that the church has for him and to try to draw him into them. However, in his experience there is an occasional person who profits from the individual relationship with the pastor but, at least for a while, cannot easily enter into the total life of the church. It seems to be frightening rather than reassuring to him, and the psychiatrist asks that ministers respect this. He suggests that clergymen be cautioned not to try to "sell" the church too fast when they sense certain resistances in the "patient."

Many of the people with whom a pastor counsels spend a period of time in the hospital where the pastor calls on them and continues to minister to them. He is always pleased when the hospital has a chaplain who can be the liaison between himself and the doctor. The next chapter aims to describe the hospital chaplain, how the movement toward clinically trained chaplains began, and some of the ways in which the chaplain serves patient, doctor, and parish minister.

CHAPTER 8

The Role of the Hospital Chaplain

The tremendous increase in the number of hospitals employing hospital chaplains indicates a concern on the part of the medical staff and administration that the whole man be considered in the healing process. Whenever a person is required to come into a hospital as a patient, this for him is an abrupt and disconcerting event. While the hospital experience may not constitute a great personal crisis for every patient, yet it provides opportunity for people to spend more time than is usual in contemplation. Realizing that the minister is in a unique relationship to people who are going through periods of stress, many hospitals have found that having a chaplain on their staff has served a very useful purpose. Chaplaincy departments are no longer in the experimental stage, and it appears that such services will soon be considered a part of standard hospital care everywhere. If hospital patients by and large do more serious thinking than people on the outside, it seems logical that wholesome direction for such thinking ought to be given patients who indicate a willingness to accept it. The professional hospital chaplain seems to offer the best answer to this need.

The chaplain is a clergyman who in addition to his regular theological education has taken considerable specialized training in the field of pastoral care. This field is a study devoted to the analysis of the relationship of the minister to people when they are under great stress. Such courses are now given in many clinical centers around the country. These include scores of mental hospitals, general hospitals, and penal institutions which for years have opened their doors to clinical training programs operated in connection with postgraduate theological schools. Before a clergyman can qualify as an accredited hospital chaplain, he must have three or more years' experience as a parish pastor in addition to a full year of clinical training at approved centers. If after he has become a professional hospital chaplain he decides that he would like to be a supervising chaplain with theological students and pastors coming to his hospital for clinical training, then he must take an additional year of residency under a supervising chaplain where a training program is in progress.

THE CHAPLAIN IN THE LARGER HOSPITAL

In the 1940's only a very few hospitals with over two hundred beds had full-time clinically trained chaplains. When the accrediting association for general hospital chaplains was formed in the mid-1940's, there were only about one or two dozen who held such positions. Within ten years the group had grown to over two hundred approved chaplains. Almost every hospital in the country is now at least considering the feasibility of establishing a chaplain's department. The American Hospital Association now has an interfaith committee on chaplaincy services to which hospitals may address their questions.

The chaplain in a hospital of two hundred beds or more could describe his day-to-day duties under perhaps five headings:

1. *Ministry to patients.* The chaplain's first concern is the patient. He has learned from experience that he cannot see every patient in the hospital, so he must choose patients for whom he can do the most good. It is the doctor and the nurse who can aid him in finding such people, for in their conversations with the patient they can often detect hidden needs which can be helped considerably by the kind of care which a pastor can give.

2. *Ministry to nurses.* The chaplain usually participates in the orientation course for all new nurses and aides who join the hospital staff. From time to time he may lead discussion groups on topics of interest to nurses. If the hospital has a school of nursing,

the chaplain teaches courses dealing with the spiritual needs of patients and the underlying Christian concerns in the health field. He also spends considerable time counseling with graduate and student nurses who wish to discuss religious and personal problems.

3. *Teaching theological students.* Many hospitals with chaplaincy departments are now training theological interns, just as for years they have been training medical interns. These young pastors (or pastors-to-be) either live in the hospital or come in daily and serve directly under the supervision of the resident chaplain. Most of these hospitals carry on this teaching program under the supervision of a theological school, the Council for Clinical Training, or the Institute of Pastoral Care. This assures that certain standards are maintained throughout the country.

4. *Interprofessional relationships.* It is easy for the chaplain to become so busy just making his own rounds that he has little time left for truly co-operative effort with attending men, residents, and interns. This is what happened in the past and it is probably why there has been so little communication between chaplains and physicians. Chaplains are therefore being urged to spend more of their time in interprofessional relationships, not only with physicians, but with psychologists, social workers, nurses, and lawyers, as well as with sociologists, anthropologists, and others whose professional interests overlap with theirs.

5. *Service to the community.* The clergymen of every community do their work in hospitals very much as do the physicians. Just as hospitals strive to maintain the highest quality of medical care, so they are also concerned about the quality of pastoral care. Until recently they assumed there was nothing they could do about it even though the administration was disturbed by the manner in which many clergymen carried on their ministry. With the coming of the hospital chaplain, many of these problems were dealt with quite effectively. The chaplain soon gets to know every minister in the community. Within a short time he arranges a regular seminar for the clergy on "Pastoral Care and Ministry to the Sick." As these men come into the hospital weekly for the

courses they have an opportunity to participate in discussions led by administrative personnel and medical staff. They appreciate the confidence placed in them by these people and the time which they give to such seminars, and in return they are more than willing to work at the improvement of their own pastoral duties. In addition to conducting such seminars, the chaplain also represents the hospital in a variety of community meetings where he interprets the work of the hospital.

THE SMALL HOSPITAL (50 beds or less)

Few hospitals of this size can afford the services of a full-time chaplain. The American Protestant Hospital Association has gone on record favoring one chaplain for every hundred beds. This means that a small hospital has to work out some special plan in order to give chaplaincy service to its patients. The following are a few methods that have been tried with some success in various communities where the hospital was too small to have a full-time chaplain.

1. Two or three small hospitals in neighboring communities have shared a chaplain in very much the same way they might share a pathologist or radiologist.

2. The local ministerial association assigns one pastor each month who spends approximately three mornings a week in the hospital acting as chaplain. He sees primarily those patients who are from out of town or who have no church affiliation.

3. In some communities there is a parish pastor who has already had specialized training in this field. He is then asked by the local hospital to spend a few mornings each week in this kind of work, with some compensation. This makes for real continuity in the relationships between chaplain and administration and staff.

4. When a small hospital is unable to secure a man through any of these suggested plans, it may then be possible to select a minister in the community who has certain aptitudes along this line and to give him opportunity to take a six- or twelve-week postgraduate course in pastoral care at a seminary. This course is not expensive and gives an exceptionally high quality of instruction

in a minimum period of time. When he returns home he continues as pastor of his local congregation, and also devotes a regular block of his time each week to the hospital.

The hospital should always assume responsibility for the appointment and employment of the chaplain. When the responsibility for selection and payment are taken over by an outside group then the hospital is never certain whose employee the chaplain is. The chaplain himself feels much more a part of the hospital family when he is appointed by the hospital board of directors and is responsible to them. He always works closely with the administrator of the hospital, and frequently a "chaplain's committee" composed of the administrator and three to five board members meets periodically with the chaplain to discuss the work of his department.

CHAPTER 9

Types of Patients a Minister Can Help

For a number of years hospital chaplains who supervise clinical training programs have been experimenting with student chaplains making rounds with doctors. At first they were not sure how patients would welcome such a joint visit, but now that literally hundreds of student chaplains have been well received by patients, they consider that making regular rounds with doctors at least once a week provides exceptionally helpful insights for the student.

As was stated previously, the hospital chaplain selects his patients with the help of doctors and nurses on the basis of finding those for whom he can do the most good. In other words, it is not to be expected that he will see every patient in the hospital every day. He must not be under the pressure of giving a good statistical report, for the new emphasis on pastoral care minimizes statistics in order to encourage a more thorough type of service to the individuals who are seen. I have said that as the chaplain introduces himself to patients, he always makes it easy for the patient to start a conversation or to terminate it. The patient then is the judge of whether or not he desires to talk with the minister concerning his particular problems.

Doctors often ask what particular types of patients a chaplain is best able to help. The following are just a few that might be mentioned, and as doctors come upon patients with such needs they might try asking a chaplain or a parish minister to look in on them. Patients with some of these needs may find that the joint approach is particularly beneficial:

1. *Patients who are lonely or who are from out-of-town.* While a minister cannot be expected to spend a great deal of time with a lonesome patient—whose very loneliness may be hindering his recovery—he usually knows of volunteer workers who are willing to see this patient on a regular basis just to visit or to read to him, write letters, or even run errands.

2. *Presurgical patients.* In some hospitals a chaplain routinely calls on all presurgical patients. While most patients do not seem to have the courage to ask for a minister, lest it frighten their relatives, yet they are glad he happened to stop by. As one patient put it, "It is an awfully good feeling to know that a minister is thinking about you when you're going to surgery." Almost all patients ask the pastor to "remember me tomorrow morning," and not a few ask for a verbal prayer while he is in the room.

When a pastor detects undue anxiety in the patient, he may offer to look in on the patient in the morning, even accompanying him to the preparation room if he desires. Anesthetists will testify to the value of the minister's brief prayer for such a disturbed patient.

3. *Patients whose anxiety is out of proportion to their illness.* These are patients who are much more worried about their illness than they should be, for their diagnosis shows nothing serious. With such a patient the minister appreciates a personal call from the doctor or a note in the chart explaining something of the situation creating the anxiety so that he may approach the patient with more understanding.

With some anxious patients the coming of a minister precipitates a flow of tears which so often seems to be necessary to clear the air before the patient and the minister can get down to business in their conversation. Where doctors happen to make rounds shortly after the minister has helped the patient "cry things out," he (the doctor) may think the reddened eyes indicate a mishandling of the problem. He had sent the minister to "cheer the patient up." Studies in clinical pastoral care have convinced pastors that superficial cheering up can sometimes actually be harmful to the patient. It is only when the patient senses that the clergyman is sufficiently interested in him to take the time to listen to his deeper worries and anxieties that he feels genuine relief from inner pressures. The tears in this case are merely a symptom of a wholesome release of what had previously been bottled up. Tears are usually not so frequent in conversations that follow.

It probably should be said here that the first appearance of a minister at the bedside of one who is going through a "trying experience" often evokes tears even from patients who were never known to express emotion openly. Hardened truck drivers who have not been in a church for years will grasp the minister's hand in a viselike grip and their eyes will cloud up with tears. Perhaps not a word is spoken between them at that time, but the patient will thank the minister on his next call for "what you did for me by just coming in to see me when I needed it most."

Physicians, then, should accept a reasonable amount of tears as normal and therapeutic in the patient-minister relationship. Religion, after all, reminds a person of childhood experiences in Sunday School, church, and home, and many of these are heavily freighted with emotion.

There is also the real possibility that the patient's abnormal anxiety is linked with a feeling of remorse and guilt for not having cleared up an unhappy relationship with some member of his family. This anxiety may have been brought on by real or imagined slights or hurts which require that he look deeply into himself. He has not dared to do this alone, but with the help of a pastor who seems to understand, he is more able to talk about these matters.

Another way to describe what is happening in such an interchange is to call it "confession." A person cannot really be "cheered up" until he has shown genuine sorrow or real guilt and an honest desire to be forgiven. Like the prodigal son, he knows that when he has sinned against another human being, he has also sinned against heaven. Sin in whatever form is never limited to earthly relationships. To a person who has at least some conception of the meaning of the Christian faith, the minister represents both Law and Love. The Law confronts the person with his daily need to examine himself. "Have I put God first— no other gods before him? Have I loved my neighbor as myself?" And the answer to these questions is always, "No, I'm guilty of having broken these laws." (For what person really puts God first in all his actions?) "Therefore, I need to admit this before I can talk freely about other things." The patient who is filled with anxiety often thinks such thoughts on beginning a conversation with a minister. If anything therapeutic is expected to happen as a result of the minister's call, there can be no short cuts to inner peace. The patient has to discover these things in himself and be willing to confess them either silently to God or privately to an- other person—pastor or layman. An enduring type of happiness will come only to the person who is willing to travel the "way of salvation" which through the centuries has meant awareness of estrangement from God, conviction of sin, sorrow and repentance, forgiveness, and newness of life. The pastor has to meet the patient where he is and proceed at the patient's own pace. In some cases the patient's emotional state may get worse before it gets better. The pastor's judgment will have to be trusted that he knows how to apply the Law and the Love of God in the right proportions and in a manner that is both healing and strength- ening.

Wherever the pastor finds that the patient's anxiety is patho- logical, he will indicate this to the physician and hope that psy- chiatric consultation will make clear the next steps in working with the patient. The minister then may limit his ministry to regular but brief calls where through appropriate Scripture read- ings and prayer he can strengthen the patient with hope and en- couragement. Until the psychiatrist has helped the patient work through the basic causes of his trouble, the minister conducts a supportive ministry.

4. *Patients whose illness will necessitate a change in their way of life.* (Heart disease, tuberculosis, stomach ulcer, high blood pressure, etc.) These are patients who have the need to talk over their enforced new way of life with a number of different people.

It is in these cases that the medical social worker is particularly helpful, for he is well aware of all the resources of the community which can be called upon to assist the patient in making his new adjustments. Such patients are not at all sure that they will be able to make such an about-face in slowing down, or taking a different job. They want to consider it from every possible angle, and the social worker is exceedingly capable of helping them to do so.

Their problems are obviously physical, psychological, *and*, I think, basically theological, for they are now required to look at the meaning of life in a new way. "As they think in their hearts" will show up in their outer actions. Their main hostility may be directed against their doctor, or their relatives, but in actuality it is also against God. They cannot admit their negative feelings against God without some help. So they might just as well get this hostility out into the open and begin to handle it immediately by talking with one of His representatives.

These patients may want to read books that deal intelligently with the matter of changing attitudes under pressure. They are grateful to a pastor who is sufficiently at home among books to be able to recommend the right ones. For some this marks the first time in their lives they have had to think deeply on religious questions.

Here the minister thinks of himself primarily as a teacher. Readjustment to a new way of life requires the rigorous process found in any learning situation, and the patient needs someone who has been over this ground before to guide him progressively toward new modes of thought.

5. *Patients with amputations, facial scars, colostomies, etc.* While these patients have many of the same problems as those in the previous category, their feelings are intensified because they feel sure that others are going to stare at them or talk about them in whispers.

For these people the clergyman, in addition to being a pastoral figure, represents the outside world. If he is able to be with them without showing evidence of being shocked by their appearance or annoyed by what they are sure is an offensive odor, the patients gain a little more courage to face the people on the outside.

6. *Patients whose illness is functional.* The pastor's basic ministry to such a person is to point him to the resources of his faith. However, a clergyman with adequate clinical training may be able to gain some insights into the patient's make-up which will be of interest to the physician.

A professional hospital chaplain will usually write his own notes on such a patient and will be eager to discuss them with the doctor. Where the doctor has worked closely with a particular chaplain and knows his abilities, the chaplain may be asked to assume a more active role in the treatment of these patients whose illness is such a complex mixture of physiological and psychological factors.

It is with the patient who is going through inner struggles that the chaplain finds a helpful teammate in the intelligent nurse. The businesslike atmosphere of the modern hospital presents some very real obstacles to the healing process. If the illness of the patient is in any way related to his inner feelings, the hospital setting does not offer the best opportunity for him to talk over his problems in an unhurried and natural way with someone who cares. In the attempt to make hospitals efficient—which they have to be—they have become so businesslike that cold routine often replaces warm concern. Yet the nurse can be a bright spot in the picture if she develops the intuitive sense for being at the patient's side at just the right time. If, in addition, she is equipped to talk with the patient in the right way at the right moment, then nursing care takes on a dimension that contributes immeasurably to the healing process. The clergyman who has learned to help people through the careful use of words is anxious to work more closely with the nurse in a ministry which might be called "the ministry of meaningful conversation." He knows that the emotionally mature nurse is his natural ally in the fight against debilitating fears and anxieties which block the flow of healing strength.

7. *Patients whose illness is terminal.* Some people think that the clergyman's primary task in the hospital is to minister to those

who are about to die. This category of patients is mentioned near the end of the list to emphasize that perhaps 90 per cent of the minister's work is with people who are soon going to leave the hospital because they are recovering from their illness. However, with the terminal patient the pastor has a special task and opportunity. By this time most of the other professional people who have been caring for this patient have more or less given up because there is really very little they can do. Some of them feel guilty about going through the motions of various kinds of treatment because they know how useless it is. During this period when no one knows quite what to do the clergyman can or at least ought to bring to the terminal patient the quiet hope and confidence of a faith which views life and death from a nonmaterial perspective. The pastor's opportunity is to demonstrate by his own concern and the words of Scripture and prayer that the patient is in the care and keeping of a loving and dependable God who is with him not only to the end of this short life, but also in the promised life to come.

8. *Patients who are in the maternity department.* The maternity ward is usually the happiest place in the whole hospital. It is hard to apply the word "patient" to the new mother for whom this new baby is a cause for genuine thanksgiving. But in the midst of her joy is always the lurking fear that maybe she is not strong enough to rear this child as she ought. Often the minister can help the mother to find new sources of strength and courage. To put it another way, in the normal, healthy mother are to be found the faint glimmerings of a deepening faith. If the clergyman can minister to her at this very important period in her life and describe in an intelligent, yet simple and natural way how she can give to her child the stability of such faith, then he will actually be making a permanent contribution to the life of the whole community. A community is only as strong as its individual families.

But occasionally even the maternity ward knows anxiety and tragedy. Such unhappiness is not always related to abnormalities. Often behind the smiling face of a new mother are a multitude of worries which she has not felt free to express to anyone. We think first of the undesired pregnancy with its economic and emotional problems. She is thinking, "We can't afford another baby," or "Bill said if we had another pregnancy it would be my fault."

Then there is the mother whose husband has decided in advance that he wants a son, but the newborn child is not a boy and he is furious about it.

Or there is the mother with the premature baby who is certain she will not be able to care for it properly.

Or there is the mother whose relationship to her husband has deteriorated so badly that she is unrealistically depending on this new child to hold the marriage together.

Or there is the mother who has a stillbirth and is trying courageously to handle all the feelings accompanying this experience.

Or there is the mother whose husband is of a different religious faith and who now faces the problems related to the baptism of the child and the inevitable unpleasantness with in-laws.

One of the most difficult of all problems has to do with the birth of an abnormal child. When institutionalization is recommended, the clergyman's point of view may be very important to the family. This suggests that it would be helpful if physicians and clergy discussed the problem of institutionalization beforehand and came to some understanding of the physical and moral implications of such decisions. When parents are called upon to make choices of such magnitude, they often want to feel that they have the approval of the spiritual leaders of the community as well as the approval of those in the medical profession.

When the emergency involves the possible death of a newborn baby, the physician or nurse usually considers baptizing the child. Before this is done, however, the religious affiliation or denomination of the parents ought to be ascertained. While most denominations believe in infant baptism, some do not. Among these are the Baptists and Disciples of Christ. It would be discourteous to say the least, and very upsetting in many cases, to proceed with the baptism of an infant when the parents may have strong convictions against such a procedure or rite. It is always advisable, therefore, not to hurry unduly with baptism until one is certain that the parents desire that it be performed. In many cases there is ample time to contact the family minister so that he, in consultation with the family, may decide the kind of religious ministry to be conducted. If the denomination involved does not practice infant baptism, the family's pastor will minister to the mother and father in a manner consistent with his church's teachings.

When the doctor or the nurse has ascertained that the family desires that the child be baptized and there is insufficient time to call in a minister, the following very simple formula for emergency baptism is used. The one conducting the baptism dips his hand in a bowl of clean water and pours a very small quantity over the head of the child, saying, "I baptize thee in the name of the Father, and of the Son, and of the Holy Ghost." With each phrase he pours the water on the infant's head. A name for the child may be used, but it is not necessary. (Those present may also pray the Lord's Prayer followed by the Benediction.) If the child lives, the usual public baptism service (of ratification) may be conducted in the church.

If it is the minister who conducts the emergency rite in the nursery, he wears cap, mask, and gown and asks the father and one or two witnesses (nurses and doctors) to assist him. The service is not more than two or three minutes in length and even though the child may be in an incubator, there is nothing about the service which will create further hazard for the baby. Later the minister gives the father a signed certificate indicating that the baptism has been performed.

Some physicians ask that the clergyman accompany them to the hospital room when the mother is to be given sad news concerning her child. After the doctor has described the situation to the mother and her initial reactions have been dealt with, the physician leaves the room and the clergyman remains. Often the shock so stuns the mother that she is unable to express her feelings at that time. Through daily calls the pastor assists her in handling her grief because often she can stand to face only a small part of her problem at a time.

The clergyman will make the necessary arrangements when a funeral service is to be held. If an autopsy and cremation would be desirable, the minister can help to explain the reasons for this.

There are certain patients for whom the minister can do more good than for others. He does his best work when he is called in by the doctor to see patients who may belong in one of these eight groups. The care he gives patients will be of a different type from that given by any other member of a helping profession. At times his approach to patients may not be exactly what the doctor had hoped for. The doctor may wish he had more opportunities to talk with the clergyman who calls on his patients about what he himself thinks about pastoral care, for he has some suggestions on how to improve it. The next chapter discusses one way in which doctors and ministers can come to grips with the joint task that is theirs. It describes in some detail a Religion-Medicine Case Conference where a dozen clergymen and physicians take time to look carefully at what happens when a clergyman goes into a sickroom. Physicians who have hesitated to refer a clergyman to a patient because of some unfortunate experiences in the past may take hope for the future. There are encouraging signs that because of the increasing number of physicians and clergymen who are meeting together in small groups to discuss cases, the quality of pastoral care will steadily improve. Most ministers are eager to discuss with doctors ways in which their own ministry to the patient can be made more helpful.

CHAPTER 10

Religion-Medicine Case Conference

To test the possibility of developing some kind of professional communication between physicians and clergymen, arrangements were made for regular Religion-Medicine Case Conferences to be held in the University of Chicago Clinics (which are integral with the Medical School of the University). A generous grant from the Chicago Community Trust (a private foundation) made it possible for a research assistant, the Rev. Alan Richardson, a doctoral candidate in the theological school, to schedule these conferences on a weekly basis and to record them for research purposes. These conferences were found to be helpful and now continue as a regular part of the teaching program in the area of religion and medicine.

To these conferences come representatives from the various professions within the clinics who are responsible for patient care —physicians, nurses, social workers, and chaplains, together with those in training for these professions. The conferences are clinical in nature and they center on a particular patient who is being seen by members of these professions. The format of each conference is the discussion of the patient from various perspectives, with special emphasis on the religious dimensions of the patient's life and the way in which the patient's attitudes toward life contribute to his illness and health.

It is, of course, clear that the patient is in the hospital primarily for medical care. The religious service to the patient is within the context of his total medical problem. Theological students who are taking a one-year course in clinical pastoral care are assigned to a medical or surgical service and attend rounds with the medical staff. It is from these day-to-day co-operative efforts that cases believed to be of teaching value are chosen for presentation at the conference.

In order to show the nature, the scope, and the benefits of this approach in both medical and religious perspectives, I shall refer to two cases. Excerpts from the tape recordings made at these conferences will be used wherever quotations are indicated. Some editorial changes were necessary both for purposes of clarity and to conceal the identity of the patients.

The first case involves a forty-year-old housewife with a case of chronic lymphatic leukemia. The physician in charge, Dr. R, presented the following data: The patient's chief complaint was recurrent swelling in the neck (of eight years' duration). She was first seen at another medical center when a diagnosis of chronic lymphatic leukemia was made. At that time she was treated with full body radiation. Her condition may be described as one of pernicity and long-term survival. A biopsy of the labial ulcer did not reveal carcinogenic degeneration. Her progress in this hospitalization was marked by slow improvement of the skin ulcers with concomitant discomfort and irritation. She was receiving small doses of oral narcotics to try to control the pain.

During her hospital stay the patient underwent a striking change in attitude. Her physician described it in this way: "Something has happened to her in the last few days—superficially, anyhow. This makes us happy, because when we go into the room now, we are not facing a woman who is tearful and very despondent about her pain and slow progress. Now she smiles and seems quite willing to accept the fact that it is going to be a long-term cure. This, I would say, on a superficial level anyhow, is a very fine attitude that we like to see patients take."

The change of which he spoke was noted by the chaplain on the third call. At first the patient complained to him about the doctors and the hospital, but then she turned to a discussion of religion. She reported that she was feeling much better and attributed this to her faith. She tended to belittle her symptoms, although she did not deny their reality. Throughout the visit she expressed her religious faith in such terms as "I am in the hands of the Master," and "I am relying on Jesus."

The question which was considered of major importance to this conference was raised by Chaplain J who visited her. "To what extent," he asked, "is her present attitude, which is akin to the 'power of positive thinking,' going to be stable enough and deep enough in its roots to support her when she realizes that she is doomed to many years of very poor health and in some cases to severe pain? Is her religious faith strong enough to carry her through these crucial times? Will the persisting pain crack this superficial kind of belief?"

The discussion which followed centered on three aspects of this general question: (1) the possible destructive effect which this religious attitude could have on the long-term welfare of the patient; (2) the methodological alternatives available to the chaplain and the physician in dealing with this patient; (3) the implications of this case for future co-operative efforts.

In the conference, Chaplain C stated that he felt the chaplain's role should be one of acceptance and willingness to stand by if the patient faltered. "The role of the chaplain here is not to go in and try to alter what she has done, but to accept this and understand it and try to understand it from her perspective. This concept of being 'in the hands of the Master' is symbolism that she is using. Treat this as a valid expression, an expression of integrity, and then be available to her to indicate to her sources of available help when she needs it, so that if things begin to shake and she doesn't feel that she is any longer 'in the hands of the Master,' she can know that she had not got herself out so far on a limb that there is no return."

Another chaplain, Chaplain A, felt that the patient's expression of faith was a means of avoiding a distressing diagnosis through fantasied religious symbolism. "Nothing that has been said so far seems to indicate anything more than the fact that this patient seems to be feeling better right now. She attributes it to some religious resources. What I am maintaining is that she is trying to talk herself out of the seriousness of her situation by using religious symbolism. This may have some temporary value for her. It may make her an easier patient to manage here at this time, but I feel that ultimately this type of approach will not support the patient and that the chaplain would have to work in terms of preparing the patient to make a shift from this inadequate kind of faith which carries her away from, or above, her illness to a kind of faith that helps her through her illness."

This comment found support from the attending physician. "Coming back to the real brunt of Chaplain A's comment, I think that this is a very valid attitude. We can't accept this kind of expression on her part *ipso facto* as authentic and sustaining until we know more about it. In this very process of subsequent visits during the next month of hospitalization we shall get to know what the chaplain really can do in this situation. The danger I see in this supportive approach of accepting her statement is that when the time comes when this attitude breaks down under some pressure, she will not be able to look to the chaplain as one who can help her, because the chaplain is the one who has gone along with the other idea. 'He felt that what I had said before was adequate and when I really had deep feelings all along he didn't really sense them. Therefore, neither the chaplain can help me nor religion and I am left without any resources at all.' If the chaplain never really accepts any of her negativities along the way, then this obviously would be a very bad idea, but if along the way he has accepted these doubts, hostilities, and negativities, then the chaplain hasn't given purely a supportive kind of treatment. It has been deeper than that. It has gone beyond that. He will have demonstrated a readiness to talk to her at a deeper level."

The immediate plan was for the chaplain to continue to see the patient in consultation with the medical staff, but it was agreed that with this patient a sustaining kind of care would be necessary after the patient left the hospital. Chaplain G made this suggestion: "If the hospital can make itself available to her in a continuing relationship, then perhaps the Chaplain's Department ought to do the same thing. Dr. R, would feel that it is in order, when you discharge a patient like this, to suggest that when she comes back to the out-patient department she should also come back to the Chaplain's Department at the same time?"

Dr. R responded, "I think that would be a very great help. I think we are going to be able with you to observe her actions for some time in the hospital, because while we are thinking now of a local excision of the ulcer, we've been turning it over in our minds that she ought to stay for at least a month now, so we probably will be able to watch this together."

The possible implications of this case for other hospital work were then considered. "Was this case a rather rare situation in which co-operative care was indicated or is this a rather common experience in the clinics?" Chaplain C asked. "Do you have other patients who come to you with problems that make you uneasy from an extra-medical point of view? Do you have some questions about the efficacy of your patients' attitudes toward life and their possible interference with the medical processes?"

The response to these questions was rather diffuse. Dr. R replied, "Well, I'm not sure that this happens very frequently, but on the other hand, it could be that it is something we haven't been taught to recognize. Now here in the case of Mrs. X, it would seem to me that I would never have noticed what was going on, at least the kinds of things which you have brought out today. I may be seeing a lot of this kind of thing and not recognizing it. We don't do too much talking about this side of a patient's life. I suppose you'd say this is the patient's reaction to a situation. Now you take a man that's up in Room 3. There's a man who has the kind of faith that seems to be what you chaplains have been talking about. He really seems to be able to face up to a life situation that is pretty awful. We doctors remark frequently concerning the tremendous courage he shows in the face of real suffering. I guess we never really thought about him as having the real thing, but if I had compared him to Mrs. X, I would have seen some differences in the two. The question now is whether what she has had will sustain her. I guess on the basis of this discussion she doesn't have the real thing."

Another physician, Dr. B, thought that perhaps this added perspective was beyond the proper function of the physician's concern. He said, "I think you ought to be aware that most of our work is pretty narrowly concerned with the physiological problems—we're interested in blood tests and in theories of therapeutical chemical reactions. Individually, they're for the most part a repository for hematological phenomena. We might as well be frank to admit this. Most of the time we don't concern ourselves with these human factors, and some of us feel that to go beyond this is really outside the limits of the physician's proper relationship to the patient. And so perhaps we don't really get involved in many of the things which psychiatrists speak of as part of the doctor's job."

This difference in the focus of the physician's task was elaborated upon by Dr. R: "Well, where I went to school, they recognized the importance of this other point of view very much—at least in a superficial fashion they stressed it, if not in a real fashion —... frequently the students will get the idea that they didn't learn a single thing in class today because the doctor spent the whole time talking with a patient about his daughter and her college problems. Many times this is the meat of the whole problem."

A second case conference centered on a person whose religious faith was of positive value in combating her illness.

Her physician, Dr. K, made the following report at the conference: "This twenty-eight-year-old housewife was first seen on referral from another physician. She had known swelling of the lymph glands of the neck for six months and a biopsy led to a diagnosis of Hodgkin's disease. Previously she had always been in good health, had been happily married for six years and had three young children. Following the establishment of the diagnosis, she was treated with X-ray therapy to the neck and chest and subsequent treatment here included more X-ray therapy and other symptomatic treatment. She never required hospitalization here until two years later, when she experienced recurrent episodes of temperature elevation and upper abdominal pain. Physical

examination and laboratory studies indicated that her recent difficulty was on the basis of abdominal Hodgkin's activity and she
was started on a course of X-ray therapy to the upper abdomen.
Her hospital course was complicated by gastrointestinal bleeding,
but the exact site of hemorrhage was never defined—although at
the time of discharge, bleeding seemed to have subsided. She was
discharged on the nineteenth hospital day, and at that time was
without fever and had obtained apparent relief of abdominal distress. X-ray treatments were to continue for a period of several
weeks on an out-patient basis."

The chaplain's analysis was then made by Chaplain A. "This
patient was referred to us by the husband and by the Clerk of
Session of their church. On my initial visit I was impressed with
how naturally and realistically the patient spoke of her illness.
There was a rare maturity and positive interpretation of the disease. This attitude has been fostered and is being maintained in a
large degree by the quality of her religious faith. Last summer
there was a severe depression during which the patient was
obsessed with the knowledge of her impending death, and there
was also a loss of psychological contact with the rest of her family. An emergency trip was made to the minister in their home
town, and as a result of this visit, the family relationships were
restored. After this trip was made, she and her husband talked
about subjects which they had previously avoided—her death, the
possibility of her husband's remarriage, and the future care of the
children. She has seen positive good resulting from this illness—
a deepening relationship with her husband, a new level of religious
faith, an incentive to a relative to enter medical school. It is my
hypothesis that patients like this one tend to vacillate between
periods of accepting their prognosis with fortitude and periods of
denying it with accompanying depression. Neither of these
periods are 'pure' in the sense that they are unmixed with the
other. Although this patient is now in a period of expressing positive feelings, there are also feelings of negativity which are operating at a less conscious level."

During the discussion that followed, a number of important

questions were raised. A theological student asked, "What relationship does this woman's religious faith bear toward her illness?" To this Dr. K replied, "Well, that's a good question. I think that everybody who had any medical contact with this lady was very much impressed that this is an individual with an attitude quite unlike those we usually see in people with an incurable disease who are aware of their condition. Frankly, I did not know of her religious faith, and I did not know to what I could attribute her attitude. I did get a chance just a few days before she left the hospital to talk with her husband at some length. He brought it to my attention that she had always been informed of everything and that they had decided to keep nothing from her, that they were quite able to face anything that we had to tell them. Frankly, it wasn't until she had left the hospital that I realized that her religious background had been what it is."

The student then inquired further, "What would you say the value was of this kind of attitude?" Dr. K answered, "Regardless of how this attitude was effected, I think that it is quite favorable in a condition of this kind, because if a person does not want to make an effort, her course can be downhill much more than otherwise. Here is a lady who is fighting. She is aware of what is going on, but she is making every effort to lead as normal a life as possible. You walk into her room and she takes immediate command of the situation. She is not an invalid. She offers you refreshment. She introduces you to relatives and friends. *She* keeps her finger on what is going on at home from her hospital bed. I think that her attitude is going to keep her going just as long as it is possible, and without this attitude I think that she would fail much more easily."

This had some important implications for the meaning of health. One chaplain spoke about health in terms of wholeness and suggested that this patient's response to her illness was in the direction of health because it involved the taking into herself, rather than the denial of, that part of her life which was both potentially destructive and potentially enriching. This, he felt, was an affirmation of life with its essential ambiguities.

The discussion turned to the other side of her feelings—the negative—which was not too much in evidence. Chaplain C suggested that as the time of death approached, these negative expressions were going to become more frequent as the physicians would have increasing difficulty in helping her. Perhaps, he thought, the role of the chaplain would then become greater.

Dr. K said, "I would like to add that part of this depression is going to be physiological rather than psychological in origin as these organs deteriorate. Especially will this be true near the end, when she is definitely terminal. Some of the expressions that she will make are going to be understandable only in the light of these physiological changes."

Dr. G concurred, "I agree with that. When she's feeling reasonably fit, when her blood count is elevated, when she's not especially weak, when she's not having a great deal of fever or pain, she is able to bring her defense mechanisms to bear quite well in taking care of her everyday situation. But at one point during this recent hospitalization, when she apparently bled down quite far, we noticed her only period of depression. When we transfused her, once again she assumed her old attitude and I think that what you say is true. There comes a point when we are not going to be able to overcome the physiological degeneration which is going on, and at that point she may not be able to maintain the same attitude she has shown for the most part so far."

On the basis of such case conferences we can draw a number of conclusions.

1. Only as a healing discipline is concerned for the care of the whole man can it adequately deal with a part. Physician and chaplain realize this increasingly at these meetings. There are aspects of the patient's life of which both should be aware if adequate care is to be given. Unless the chaplain is aware of the nature and the course of an illness, he is ill-prepared to minister to the patient as a whole person in a total situation. And unless the physician is aware of the relationship between the patient's religious faith and attitude toward life and his medical situation,

certain patterns of behavior and certain important changes in the patient's condition will be inexplicable or unattended.

2. No single healing discipline can care for the whole man, but through active co-operation with other disciplines, something approaching total care is possible. A great deal of literature in the field of medicine is concerned with this wholistic, total approach to patient care. Religious literature has been similarly concerned. Especially in a hospital setting where the sick person is visited both by the physician and the chaplain or pastor is it important to learn to communicate, if the patient is going to have optimum care.

3. Religion can play either a positive or a negative role in the healing process. Generally speaking, faith which is open, reality-centered, and constructive engenders health-enhancing attitudes. Ministers feel that there are unhealthy religious attitudes which are definitely destructive. There are great qualitative differences in religious faith which may be crucial in combating illness and in attaining better health. Only as both physicians and ministers move toward an understanding of the various ways in which religion may help or hinder the patient will more significant conversations be possible among them.

4. Doctors and chaplains are finding that communication barriers are not nearly so insurmountable as might be anticipated. Both groups have a unique technical language and a specialized function, but there are large areas in which linguistic and professional differences can be overcome. Such efforts not only enrich the several disciplines, but they also have beneficial results in the improved care of the patient.

One of the areas in which communication could be improved has to do with how ministers and doctors handle the truth in the presence of patients with terminal illness. The constant dilemma encountered in such situations should prompt an effort to understand the problem from many different points of view. The chapter which follows indicates the questions with which we must wrestle if we are to be as sensitive as we need to be in the care of the terminal patient.

CHAPTER 11

To Tell or Not To Tell
(Terminal Illness)

Clergymen have difficulty ministering to terminal patients who do not know the seriousness of their condition. The clergyman's hands are tied in giving pastoral care because he feels awkward and uneasy whenever the patient shows interest in discussing matters which are being withheld from him. In order not to antagonize the physician or the family, the clergyman is required to carry on innocuous conversations and change the subject to lighter matters whenever there is danger of moving toward more profound thoughts.

Here is a situation, for example, where one of two middle-aged maiden sisters had cancer. The doctor and the other sister chose not to tell the sick sister and informed the pastor of this. After several strained pastoral calls in which they talked mostly about the weather, the patient broke down and told the pastor that she knew all along that she had cancer. She had kept silent about it because she felt it was her duty to play the game so as not to upset her sister. She said that every visit from both her sister and the pastor had been like a nightmare, and she was completely exhausted after they left "from putting on an act." The patient wondered if the doctor would mind if she and her sister spoke openly about it. The pastor was sure the doctor would understand. But when he spoke to the doctor about it the response was, "Why do you ministers always want to talk about death?"

Ministers do not like to be thought of as morbid and, rather than make too much of an issue of it, they have said little about it. They know that the doctor is somewhat justified in his statement. Some parsons do use the deathbed as a place to give the patient the "third degree." But the growing mood among most pastors is to minister to terminal patients in quite a different manner. They accent the love and mercy of God. No sermons are preached *at* the patient. In the conversation the patient is free to discuss or withhold whatever is on his mind. When the patient senses that no pressure is being put on him he then expresses some of his fears and anxieties which he has not previously dared put into words. What he had been holding in has caused him indescribable inner pain. Now it comes out like a geyser. The air is cleared and the pastor can carry on meaningful conversations with the real person. There is no longer need for sham or pretending.

Not telling the truth often boomerangs. A man of thirty-five took his father to a doctor to have an abdominal pain diagnosed. An exploratory operation was indicated. At surgery it was discovered that the father had an inoperable cancer. The doctor and the son decided not to tell the truth to this sixty-year-old father. He lived for two years and during that time his family continually told him he was getting better. Never during those years did the father have an opportunity for a serious conversation with any member of his family. Even the minister was forced by the family to carry on a ministry which was something of a farce. The father became more and more detached from the family as they shied away from any real communication with him, and he finally died in isolation from them. Shortly after his death, the son had similar abdominal pains. He went to the same doctor and at surgery it was found that he did *not* have a malignancy. He was told this but refused to believe it, saying, "Doctor, you were an awfully good actor when you told my father the same thing. Now I cannot believe you." He went through months of torment, positive that he too had been tricked. It was only as he retained his health with none of his father's later symptoms that he was willing to believe the diagnosis. Yet, always there was this insidious doubt that his cancer was the slow-growing kind. When a doctor becomes known as a good actor in concealing the truth, there will be times when people will hesitate to have full confidence in him.

We are not suggesting a cold or blunt telling of the truth to every patient. There are many exceptions and each patient will respond differently. There should be no rule one way or the other. The tendency in the past was not to tell the patient; we now question this point of view because it is not appropriate in many situations. It has often brought mental suffering to patients by walling them off from their families at the most crucial moment in their lives. This is particularly true with married couples who for years have shared every crisis with each other. It was their sharing of these crises which deepened their love and increased their appreciation of the blessings of marriage. Certainly if one of them is facing death it would be cruel to tear them apart just when they could mean the most to each other. If we believe that man can transcend his ordinary self at such a time then the two should have the privilege of meeting the experience together.

To tell or not to tell this patient may not be entirely a medical decision, and to make a more balanced decision it may be well to include the patient's minister as well as the family in the consultation. This will depend, of course, on the relation of the patient and family to the minister.

The church believes in telling the patient the truth whenever it will be medically or spiritually beneficial to do so. There is no hard-and-fast rule which can be made because of the wide variety of individuals and the circumstances within which the terminal problem must be faced.

There are ways and ways of telling patients the truth. Never say to a patient, "You are going to die." The truth is told in love and with genuine concern for the feelings of the patient. With some it must be given in small doses; with others all the medical details are given; with still others few if any words are spoken, for it is clear that they cannot bear to discuss it. However, the knowing glances which pass between doctor and patient and the absence of foolish superficial gaiety means that the information has been conveyed to the patient.

For some patients very little will ever be said about death in the doctor's presence. They may continue the discussion with those dearest to them. Often visitors who know that the patient has been told the truth wonder how he can seem so unconcerned about it. Experience has shown that these patients are not unconcerned about such a diagnosis, but they face this fact just as they have faced many other difficulties in life. They tend to follow the pattern they have built up through life. They take a day at a time and refer to death only when particular decisions have to be made. They are not morbid about it, just realistic. And it is in this mood that they talk with their minister. The Christian faith has always been realistic in facing man with his finitude, for death is no new subject which must be studiously avoided until a person finds himself face-to-face with it.

One man with a terminal disease said, "I am really not afraid of death and I am grateful that you were frank with me. I have many things I would like to do. Suspecting, but not knowing for certain what my condition was, proved worse than knowing for sure. I feel somewhat relieved because now I can set my course and follow it. After all a man can't expect to live forever."

Other patients will be so shocked by the news that for a time they will be unable to discuss it at all. Then later when the full impact hits them they talk and cry and talk and talk until they have had a chance to express how they feel inside. At first this may be very difficult for the family. Then they see that no longer do they have to try to remember the last lie they told. And in this atmosphere of openness and honesty there is the possibility for real growth in both the patient and his family. These are the primary conditions necessary for spiritual growth to take place. Any number of patients and family members have matured beyond the fondest hopes during these final months. Some patients who have been unnecessarily shielded from the fact of death may be done a disservice, for this may keep them from experiencing the joy of real communication with those they love.

The Christian point of view encourages man to realize that he is made for more than just this life. It is believed that in God's plan for man there is something beyond the experience of this life and that such a vital faith is a source of amazing strength. When a person holds such a faith he lives differently, even victoriously, in the midst of what the world might call a tragic situation. It changes his whole perspective and he lives by the conviction that this life is not the end for him, but that God has other plans for him. In this Christian hope one sees anew the inherent worth of man in the eyes of God.

The greatest tribute that can be paid to the dignity of man is to entrust him with the truth about himself so that, if he has the strength, he can make his own decisions. This freedom must never be taken from him.

WHEN DEATH IS IMMINENT

When the physician feels that a certain patient may die within a day or two, a clergyman should be notified of the patient's condition. If the patient is in a coma the pastor will minister primarily to the family. If the patient is able to converse, then the clergyman should always be given a few moments completely alone with him to ascertain his particular spiritual needs. It may be necessary for the physician to arrange to clear the room for a few minutes while the pastor talks personally with the patient. Special nurses should leave the room. The doctor will know how long the patient can be without medical assistance and can indicate this to the pastor.

A clergyman may be severely handicapped in his ministry to a patient if even one person (particularly a member of the family) remains in the room. He is practically helpless in getting people to leave the room unless the doctor assists him in arranging for such moments. The relatives usually keep hovering around or insist that a doctor or nurse always be in attendance. One physician counteracts this by saying to the relatives, "Let's give the patient a chance to talk with the minister. This is just as important as anything I can do for the patient."

When the patient has expired, the minister usually offers a prayer of thanksgiving for the life of this person and in this way dignifies the passing of a human soul. Relatives frequently comment later that they will never forget "the solemnity of that moment when the minister came in and prayed as father was dying." This *should* be a solemn moment, and the minister should go out of his way to share such moments at the bedside of a dying patient.

What has begun as a ministry to a terminal patient often shifts to a ministry to the *relatives* of the terminal patient. As the terminal patient becomes progressively worse the pastor finds that close relatives frequently ask for help in many subtle ways. Their growing need centers around the natural anxiety which arises as they begin to face the fact that they will have to continue to live without the presence of this person who has been so closely related to many decisions they have made in their own lives. They find themselves wrestling with intense feelings which vacillate between open rebellion against everything and everyone, and passive dependence upon any relative or friend who is willing to make every decision for them. The power of these emotions is so great that it is important to analyze what happens to a person who faces a serious loss in his life and how this grief may affect even his own state of health.

CHAPTER 12

The Grief Process and Health

The way in which a person grieves over the loss of something important in his life has a startling effect upon health. Grief is involved in many of the situations of life in addition to those related to the death of a loved one. It is entirely possible that a large proportion of functional and spiritual illness is brought about by the loss of someone or something that means a great deal to a person. Because the doctor and the minister confront grieving patients and parishioners almost daily, they should be cognizant of grief's potential relationship to illness.

In a typical day the doctor may see a person who has been ill for many months who is grieving over his separation from his family; or a person who is grieving over the loss of an amputated limb; or a father who has physical symptoms arising from grief over the loss, through marriage, of his only daughter. Similarly the minister will see grief in process in such people as a new family in the community who are grieving over their separation from former friends; or a father grieving over a prodigal son; or a person grieving over the loss of his religious faith, a faith which had been adequate in his childhood, but not in the world he now faces.

Everyone grieves at some time or other and certainly it is a very normal experience. A person tends to follow a normal pattern as he works through the loss of something very important to him. Of course, a person can carry too far any of the normal aspects of grief so that they become abnormal or pathological. It would

be helpful if more people understood the normal grief process
which follows an important loss so they would not be so frightened by these normal symptoms when they observe them in
themselves. A certain amount of objectivity concerning the
process may save a number of people from panic. For this reason
ministers should devote one sermon each year to the grief process.
While no two people go through this process in exactly the same
way, it is possible, to some extent, to predict typical stages
through which most people will pass. These typical stages are:
(1) shock; (2) emotional release; (3) inability to concentrate
on anything but the lost object; (4) symptoms of physical distress; (5) feelings of depression and gloom; (6) sense of guilt;
(7) sense of hostility; (8) unwillingness to participate in the
usual patterns of conduct; (9) gradual realization that withdrawal
from life is unrealistic; and finally (10) readjustment to reality.
    Obviously, not everyone will go through each of these stages,
nor necessarily experience the stages in this order. The point is
that many people could have been saved untold hours of agony
if they had been told in advance that such grief was normal and
necessary in working through to a new plan of living. There
is never any certainty as to how long it will take a person to
formulate new and satisfactory patterns of life. Much depends
on his own constitutional make-up, the way he has previously
reacted to similar situations, and the way he reacts to those
around him. Usually three months to three years is sufficient time
for a person to work through a significant loss.
    1. *Shock.* Some people never go through the stage of shock
and are immediately able to express their emotions. But many
are so stunned by their loss they are unable to face it realistically
and go about somewhat dazed. They may act quite normally in
their relations to people and to necessary tasks, but there is no
expression of emotion commensurate with the tragedy which has
befallen them. This is described as the denial mechanism at work,
and it is the psyche's way of keeping a person from going to
pieces. If it is a normal shock experience the person will slowly

become aware of what has happened and face up to it emotionally at a time somewhat removed from the moment of crisis. Usually a person is in a state of shock for only a few minutes to a few days. If it persists longer than that, medical care is indicated.

2. *Emotional release.* The beneficial effects of crying have been discussed earlier. Of course, there is always the person who cries overmuch and this type of hysterical reaction may lengthen the grief process. He must be helped to see that one does not have a "nervous breakdown" because one expresses a legitimate feeling. The human psyche is much more rugged than imagined, and a person can withstand great sorrow and loss provided he is not required to bottle up his emotions. It is unnecessary to be shielded against emotional outbursts. In fact, the complete avoidance of tears can cause inner destruction.

3. *Inability to concentrate on anything but the lost object.* During this stage the person may try very hard to think about other things, but finds it impossible to do so. He is constantly preoccupied with the loss no matter where he goes. Well-meaning friends may seek to divert his thinking, but in the early stages of grief this is not only impossible, but somewhat cruel. This diversionary tactic is used too often by those who go back to the home of the bereaved after the funeral. They try every device "to get Mary to think of something besides Tom's death." It is interesting to note in this connection that according to an old Jewish custom the first meal after the funeral is prepared by a neighbor and is called the "meal of consolation." The rabbis prescribe that the topic of conversation is to be centered around the dead person, thus allowing the mourners to express their sense of loss. This is realistic, for the only subject the mourners care to discuss is the departed one.

4. *Symptoms of physical distress.* It is unusual for one undergoing grief to sleep or eat normally. This may be followed by the loss of weight or functional illness of some type, particularly headaches or backaches or feelings of oppression in the chest. These symptoms, like the other reactions to grief, must be under-

stood as temporary. They may even be helpful to the person, for they force him to focus on something physiological that requires attention.

5. *Feelings of depression and gloom.* At this stage the person feels that there is no real reason for continuing to live. He may have thoughts of total withdrawal from normal life and even of suicide. When people attempt to cheer him up, he has to resist the desire to order them away. He is gloomy, and often a person will not come out of this stage of depression until some unusual experience shocks him out of it.

6. *Sense of guilt.* This sense of guilt is closely related to the feeling of depression, for these people begin to think of the many things they wish they had done differently with regard to the deceased. It is as if they have to atone for their sins by punishing themselves with total dejection and unhappiness. When a person feels guilty some of this guilt is real and some is neurotic. It is to be expected that there will always be real guilt following the loss of one with whom there was a deep and long relationship. How can two people be so close without having hurt each other from time to time? Thus these unhappy experiences come rushing back into memory, and because the person is now dead and there is no way to ask and receive forgiveness, it is doubly difficult to work through these powerful emotions of guilt. When such a person is able to express or confess feelings of guilt to a person whom he respects, much relief is experienced. And when the person sees his guilt as having religious dimensions, he will need to work through his guilt in a way that will include real awareness of the forgiveness of God.

Even in the case of a mentally healthy person, real guilt is often accompanied by neurotic guilt. One always thinks of many things that ought to have been done, and so the sins of omission loom up as large as the sins of commission. It is to be hoped that the neurotic aspect will remain minimal.

7. *Sense of hostility.* Closely related to guilt are the feelings of hostility, which in turn make one feel more guilty. This hostility may be directed toward the doctor "who should not have

operated on mother," or the nurse "who was so busy with the other patients she neglected mother," or the member of the family "who should have done something about this sooner." In reality all these hostile feelings may be the person's way of avoiding his real feelings of hostility toward God whom he feels is ultimately responsible. Others in their hostility toward God show it indirectly by striking out at the minister who did not visit mother as often as they thought he should. This hostility, in its severe forms, is usually felt early in the grief process, but in milder forms, hostility may continue to express itself months later when it is least expected.

8. *Unwillingness to participate in the usual patterns of conduct.* One of the reasons that the person who has suffered the loss of a loved one is unwilling to get back into former activities is that he feels he would be disloyal to the deceased if he were to enjoy life again. This is one of the most difficult experiences to work through. The mourner discovers that on the day after the funeral everybody does take up life again. For most of the friends the loss of this dear one will make little or no real difference. The mourner unconsciously seeks to protest against this indifference by resisting all attempts to return to active life. As long as he resists, he is reminding others of the loss. Once he gives in he is certain that even the memory of his loved one will be wiped out. It is for this reason that those who mourn are grateful to the visitor who talks easily and naturally about the one who died. While such a conversation may bring forth tears, it is far better than purposely avoiding the subject. What bothers the bereaved most deeply is the discovery that people tend to forget because few people really care very much about another's sorrow.

9. *Gradual realization that withdrawal from life is unrealistic.* For people going through a normal grief reaction, the day finally arrives when they find that a few rays of sunshine are beginning to come through their darkened sky. These people are nearing the end of their grief pattern because they have accepted and worked these intense emotions through to some kind of satisfac-

tory new adjustment to the world around them, as well as to the world within them. Another way to put it is that they have expressed their deeply felt emotions in a manner that is creative. It is quite clear now that growth toward a mature handling of all forms of loss can take place only when a person has successfully wrestled with his most intense emotions.

10. *Readjustment to reality*. An eventual readjustment does not mean that the wound of sorrow has left no scar. There is always a scar. However, the person has realized that he can sublimate his sorrow in a number of ways and particularly in a helpful relationship to other people who are working through a grief experience. Once the person has begun to move back into life he must be reminded that although his major grief work has been done, he will still go through smaller cycles in which he will repeat some of the same phases in less severe form. There may again be periods of emotional outburst and he should not let them frighten him. He can expect times when it will be hard to concentrate, times of depression, moments of real physical distress and, for a long time, feelings of guilt and hostility. But once he has gone through his major work the succeeding battles with these emotions can more easily be won. He has learned that real growth toward the type of maturity he desires requires the quality of wrestling he has been doing. This has helped him to be unafraid to face reality in whatever form it presents itself.

In the handling of grief, there are at least three things to remember. First, a person should express as much grief as he actually feels through the normal, healthy channels of prayer and conversation. Second, he must realize that though the loss of this person is almost unbearable he must force himself, with the help of God, to function again as an individual apart from the close relationship he previously had with the loved one. Finally, the person must be reminded that he cannot live unto himself alone and that the Christian fellowship encourages those who have lost loved ones to replace the emptiness at least partially by continued relationships with other people in activities of service to mankind and even allowing one or more people to fill the emptiness in a particularly meaningful way.

In the next chapter we will present the case of Mrs. X, a hospital patient who was certain in her own mind that her illness was moving toward death. Although her physician had never told her so, she was convinced that she had only a few months to live, and she was right. Mrs. X was essentially a lonely woman who was unable to communicate her grief and basic religious anxiety to anyone because no one ever really listened to what she was saying. She gave the impression to everyone that she was a self-contained, intelligent woman who had a mind of her own and who often was outspoken in stating her position on a variety of issues. From the chaplain's later contacts with her he learned that she was unable to share her grief even with her sisters because, when they visited her, they insisted on keeping the conversation light and airy. When her daughter had asked a minister to call on her, the minister took the patient's defensiveness literally and fought her rather than trying to understand her. She literally had *no one* to whom she could talk. One might say that this was her own fault. Yet it was not all her own fault because no one had taken the time to try to understand what was back of all this defensiveness. When the chaplain came to know her better he found that all she was trying to do was to maintain her own integrity in the presence of people who wanted her to be something she could not be.

In the case of Mrs. X we will see some of the strong emotions at work which have been described in this chapter on grief, for she was in the midst of her own grief work. It was some days later before she was able to discuss with the chaplain her basic concerns regarding her coming death and her dread of "non-being." In this one interview Mrs. X, who probably represents a large segment of the nonchurchgoing population, kept her defenses up until she was certain that the other person respected her right to have convictions of her own. We will see how a pastor first bungled such an interview because of his own defensiveness. Then as he sought to understand what lay back of this person's convictions real rapport was achieved. For most of her life Mrs. X had been separated from those close to her because of the unwillingness of either side to try to understand the other. Loneliness and grief were the natural results of this detachment from loved ones.

CHAPTER 13

The Patient Who Objects to Organized Religion A Case Study

In order to enable the doctor better to understand the role of the minister or chaplain, it might be advantageous to illustrate a pastoral conversation in a hospital situation. Doctors seem particularly hesitant about having a clergyman visit a patient who is not a churchgoer. Therefore, we have chosen a patient who has negative feelings about religion in order to make doctors aware both of the difficulties the minister will encounter and of the ways in which he can overcome them.

Mrs. X is an intelligent forty-one-year-old woman who has cancer. She represents the one-third of the population of the United States with no religious affiliation who have some strong feeling against organized religion. This woman is unusually able to articulate her negative feelings so that the minister is required to deal with them.

It is well to recognize that the clergyman is often unable to minister effectively to a person like Mrs. X because (a) he does not bother to find out why such hostility to religion exists, (b) these people perceive him more as a salesman for an organization than as one who comes to serve their needs, and (c) these persons are preconditioned by previous bad experiences with religion and so set up hindrances to real "meeting." As will be noted, the clergyman in this case study started out poorly but did better as he went along.

The student chaplain, a young pastor, had just finished seeing several patients and was about to leave the floor when the head nurse said, "Mrs. X is from out of town and does not have much company. She has an inoperable cancer. Tomorrow she is going home, but she will be back in a few weeks. She has been rather lonesome and I think it would help her to talk with a minister. She is a forty-one-year-old divorceé with a daughter about sixteen." The chaplain took the nurse's advice and his conversation with Mrs. X was as follows:

Chaplain: "Good afternoon Mrs. X. I am Chaplain Blank, one of the chaplains in the hospital."

Mrs. X: "Hello." [Said without any enthusiasm.]

Chaplain: "The nurse tells me that you are going home tomorrow. I thought I would stop by and get acquainted with you before you go."

Mrs. X: "That was nice of you, but I am well now and you don't need to stop by and pray for me." [Said rather flatly so that the chaplain does not know how to take it. He finds himself responding to the underlying sarcasm and being defensive about it.]

Chaplain: "Maybe well persons need prayers more than sick ones!" [If he had said this with a chuckle it would have been all right, but she immediately senses that he has his dander up a bit and is upset by her statement, so she hits him with more.]

Mrs. X: "That may be true, chaplain, but I don't even believe in God." [People do not usually say this to a minister. They are too polite to do so, but Mrs. X enjoys a good argument, particularly with ministers, many of whom she has upset in her lifetime.]

Chaplain: "I suppose there are a number of people who don't believe in God." [He is so bothered he does not know what else to say and she can sense it.]

Mrs. X: "I'm sorry. I probably should not tell a minister things like that." [She might as well add. "You poor little minister. You can't take things like this, can you, without getting all upset." And he is so upset he allows himself to become sarcastic.]

Chaplain: "You feel that there are better people to talk to about such things." [He walks right into the trap Mrs. X has set for him.]

Mrs. X: "It is not that. It is just that ministers all believe in God and they don't care to listen to anyone who doesn't." [This statement expresses the feelings of perhaps most of the people not affiliated with churches or synagogues. They think of the minister as the "preacher" who does all the talking and never stops long enough to listen to what someone else believes. And if he does listen he tells them they are wrong anyway, so why bother to talk to him. At least Mrs. X has the honesty to tell this to a minister's face.]

Chaplain: "You feel that the person who believes in God can't understand the person who doesn't?" [For the first time the chaplain realizes that this is not a debate. This is a woman who is going through a crisis experience and who is trying to make herself understood to a person who represents an organization for which she has no use.]

Mrs. X: "It's something like that. I don't believe in God the way other people do. I don't believe that there is such a thing as a God who is a person or a spirit. If there is any God, it is in the form of a cosmic force that ends with the life of an individual. To me it's silly to believe in immortality. I believe that once you die, your life is over." [Here Mrs. X does what we have observed in so many people. When we stop arguing and try to understand what people are trying to tell us, they immediately stop being totally on the defensive and move tentatively toward what resembles a conversation in which each person is listening and responding to what the other says.]

Chaplain: "Experience has taught you that this is the way life is." [Whenever the minister listens to what people are saying, he is listening to a description of the meaning of life based on the sum total of their experiences. He must recognize their right to have come to certain conclusions. However different these opinions are from his own, he owes it to these individuals, as personalities sacred in the eyes of God, to listen thoughtfully and to attempt to understand them.]

Mrs. X: "I can't say that this is the way life is for everyone, but it is the way I have found it. This may surprise you, but I pray quite often." [In sensing that she is not going to get preached at, Mrs. X mellows and gives the chaplain a little glimpse of the part of her that is religious enough to want to pray.]

Chaplain: "You find prayer to be of some value." [To say, "See, I told you so, you do believe in prayer," would merely precipitate a debate. A pastoral conversation is not a battle of wits, it is "deep calling unto deep." Mrs. X is trying to express something which is very meaningful to her, and even though her comment about prayer seems out of context, the chaplain will only hurt the relationship by pouncing on the lack of logic. If this is important to the discussion, it will come out later.]

Mrs. X: "I don't pray like most church people, asking God to give them something. If you ask me, I think that is very crude. When I pray I sort of pray to myself, just being grateful for life, but I don't ask for anything."

Chaplain: "You don't feel that prayer is answered."

Mrs. X: "That is right. I don't feel that there is anyone who can answer prayer. I know you don't believe that way and sometimes I wish I did not believe that way, but that is the only way I can believe." ["... and sometimes I wish I did not believe that way ..." is the expression of the wistfulness of the human heart to be found in every person. When a person is going through a crisis there is usually more than average readiness to consider the possibility that perhaps he or she is made for communion with God.]

Chaplain: "You wish there were someone who could answer prayer." [Here the pastor is willing to reflect upon her wish within the context of her negative feelings because these feelings are just as much a part of her as her positive feelings, but if he stops her flow of negative feelings by pressing her positive ones, he will turn off real communication.]

Mrs. X: "I don't know. I do know that when I was in college I became very ill and I prayed to God to help me get well. I told him that I would become a Christian if he would make me well. But I had a long-drawn-out recovery from pneumonia and if it had not been for the doctors I would have died. I decided then that if God could not answer the prayers of a poor dying girl, there must be no God." [Again there is faulty logic in her argument. But in discussing the matter of belief, logic is not so important. However much we might like to see ourselves as objective and scientific, we are anything but objective about close relationships. Thus the minister does not press the issue with Mrs. X. Instead he asks a factual question.]

Chaplain: "Was that the only time you ever asked God for anything?"

Mrs. X: "No, about five years ago I asked God for help during a sickness, and just like before, I received no answer. That was the last time as far as I was concerned." [Some religious people might think that this is the time for the minister to give her some instruction on the various levels of prayer and show her how childish are her requirements of God. But it is useless to appeal to the intellect before the feelings of hostility have been tempered by a genuine desire to inquire for other ways of looking at these events. Mrs. X has not asked for such instruction or clarification and cannot be helped until she does so.]

Chaplain: "You feel that if God can't be found in the big things in life then he surely can't be found in the ordinary affairs of daily living." [Now the chaplain is listening carefully to what he believes Mrs. X is trying to say and then attempts to express her sentiments in his own words so that she can correct him if he is wrong.]

Mrs. X: "I was looking for a certainty that would remove all doubt from my mind. I don't see how one can believe in God and still have any doubts about him." [She accepts the pastor's statement as correct and moves on from there to tell him how she feels about doubt. Had he been wrong she would have told him so and he would have had to try again.]

Chaplain: "Doubt for you is a rather negative thing?"

Mrs. X: "We know so much about everything else. It seems as if it should not be expecting too much to know at least as much or more about God. Really I don't think that there is much more to us than our bodies. When our bodies have ceased to exist, I feel that that is the finish for us." [Now Mrs. X returns to her negative feelings regarding belief in God. For a time it looked as if she were moving toward some kind of faith, but now she is back again where she started. But this is life! The ambivalent feelings which people have concerning faith and doubt is one of the major themes of the Bible and it does not try to minimize this problem. Any pastoral conversation includes a movement back and forth between faith and doubt. This is one of the purposes of the gathering together of Christians in weekly worship, that they may strengthen one another's faith. It is not easy for a lone person to maintain his faith in the midst of the daily problems confronting him.]

Chaplain: "It is difficult for you to believe that there is a quality about man that might be called spiritual."

Mrs. X: That is the way it is for me, but I know that you have found it to be different."

Chaplain: "Have you always believed this way?"

Mrs. X: "No, when I was a small girl I went to Sunday School regularly. My mother died when I was young and my father spent most of his time in a saloon. Consequently, I just quit going to Sunday School. I was pretty well mixed up about what I believed until I attended college. It was then that I met people who had done a lot of thinking about these things and they were able to show me what life was really like."

Chaplain: "By this you mean that they saw life without the obstruction of religious faith?"

Mrs. X: "I mean that they did not believe things without first seeing them proved. They did not set out to destroy faith; they wanted to build a faith on facts rather than on belief."

Chaplain: "I suppose the person of Christ did not make much sense to these people."

Mrs. X: "My friends thought of Christ as a great teacher and a man with great wisdom, but some of his deeds seemed a little fantastic."

Chaplain: "You could approve of his wisdom, but not of his deeds of love."

Mrs. X: "It isn't that I disapprove of his deeds; it is just that it is impossible to understand how he did them. You might be surprised to know that I have a daughter sixteen years of age who is a faithful member of the church. She has found a faith and I don't feel that I have a right to stand in the way of her faith. She has found something that I didn't, and I won't interfere."

Chaplain: "You feel that she has found something which she needs while you haven't."

Mrs. X: "I suppose that is nearer to the truth than the way I would say it. I would say that she has found something in life in a different way than I have."

Chaplain: "In other words you have a type of faith, but it is different from your daughter's."

Mrs. X: "Yes, I would say that. I have always really rebelled against being told what to believe. I suppose if I gave up some of my rebellion I would find that my faith would be something like my daughter's."

Chaplain: "This is something you might do if you could do it and feel as if you did it on your own without someone pushing you into it."

Mrs. X: "Something like that. [Pause.] Gee, I never knew ministers were like you. Most of them can't talk intelligently about religion. They begin by trying to force you to believe something. My daughter brought her minister in to see me. He began by asking me if I was saved. I told him I wasn't interested in being saved and then he told me I would go to hell if I wasn't saved. Well, I don't believe in hell so that didn't scare me as he thought it would. I know that my daughter was embarrassed, but I hate people who try to force things on me."

Chaplain: "You want your faith to come from within."

Mrs. X: "Something like that. I can tell that you have a strong faith. I'll bet you don't have many doubts."

Chaplain: "Have you ever stopped to consider that doubt can be a great motivating force to lead one to a faith?"

Mrs. X: [Slowly and thoughtfully.] "I hadn't thought of it in that way. You mean that maybe I need to doubt some of my old doubts and get some new doubts?"

Chaplain: "By that you mean you may have doubted the wrong things."

Mrs. X: "That is what I mean."

Chaplain: "I see it is getting along toward suppertime. I've certainly enjoyed meeting you."

Mrs. X: "Thanks for stopping by even though I am going home."

That was the end of the conversation. The length of the call was about fifteen minutes. The chaplain felt that in this particular case he should not stay longer. They had begun to understand and appreciate each other's point of view, and that was about as much as could be expected in a first interview. In one way it was unfortunate that Mrs. X was leaving the hospital the next day in that the conversations could not be continued, yet any attempts to press for further goals would have been unrealistic. A great deal had happened to both the patient and the minister, and the patient needed time to think more deeply about where she should go from there. She had found another human being who recognized her as an individual with the inherent right to believe as her conscience dictated and the right to revise her beliefs when new evidence indicated that she ought to doubt some of her present doubts.

Mrs. X returned to the hospital after being home about a month. She had been in her room only a few hours when she asked the nurse to have the chaplain come in to see her. Unfortunately, the student chaplain who had ministered to her had returned to his parish and was no longer on the hospital staff. Another chaplain answered her call and she was obviously disappointed that her friend was gone. She said, "That young chaplain made a lasting impression on me. When I got home I told all my friends that I had never met a minister like him. I said that he was the first minister who really cared about what *I* thought about things. Do you suppose I can talk to you the way I talked to him?" The new chaplain assured her that she could. During the next six weeks before her death she wrestled with the major issues of life and death in a way that indicated she had long been a conscientious seeker after the truth. She had been hindered in her search by small people who had thrown emotional roadblocks in her way. The chaplain later said regarding her, "She died a Christian, of that I am convinced. But up to the very end she reserved the right to be a protesting Christian, and this was for me a truly exciting encounter with a fellow human."

PART III

Psychiatry as it Relates to Minister and Doctor

CHAPTER 14

The Bridge Function of the Clergyman

Clergymen are frequently called upon to serve a bridge function as they work with parishioners whose illness is more psychological than physiological. These patients with functional illness challenge the team concept of minister and doctor and are the problem people in medical practice. They are definitely ill, but their illness is such a complex mixture of physical malfunctioning and unhealthy attitudes that the physician finds himself in a dilemma as to how best to approach their complaints. These patients are at the same time apologetic and angry at having such a vague illness. If their illness is wholly or actually "in their mind" they want somebody to show them how to get it out. They wish it could be cut out like an appendix. They insist that nobody takes them seriously.

The physician often considers the possibility of referring this type of patient to a psychiatrist. This is a logical step but it has two barriers. First of all, many people are not willing to go to a psychiatrist because they do not think of him as working with normal people. Then too, there are not enough psychiatrists to meet the needs of all troubled people. In fact, there are large areas of the country which do not have even one psychiatrist.

This explains in part why many doctors have begun to draft ministers to talk with functionally ill patients. Before progress can be made in treating their physical symptoms these people need to speak to someone about their family, their job, and their philosophy of life. Ministers find that during a physical crisis such people progress faster toward spiritual insight than when everything is going smoothly, for there is more willingness to look within themselves. The possibility of bringing about deeper and thus more lasting changes in attitudes is therefore greater. And patients work even harder at this if their doctor is the one who encourages them to do so.

The minister is not unaware that their basic motive for coming to him is a desire to have physical health. However, he hopes eventually to get them to realize that some things are even more important than physical health. Patients often approach the minister with the thought that if they get their religious life straightened out, then their stomach problem will clear up. This may actually happen, but such a motive is hardly praiseworthy. It is the minister's task to take the patient where he is and hope to show him that the person, unlike the animal, can still live a useful and productive life despite physical difficulties. In other words, people should be prepared for the fact that while they may never enjoy complete physical health, because the symptoms may have developed too far, this need not keep them from being inwardly healthy and able to face each day's problems maturely.

While the minister is willing to assist the physician with certain patients, physical health is not his only or even his major goal. If physical health should come as a result of readjusting spiritual attitudes, well and good, but the patient must never be taught that a closer relationship to God will cure his illness. God should be loved for other reasons. There develops a sense of oneness with the creator, a new quality of love for one's neighbor, and a quiet confidence in the worthfulness of life.

What more could be wanted of life? Health, good and dependable friends, a long life, and a certain measure of prosperity could be desired. But most of the great Christians of history never had these gifts, and yet their outstanding contributions to the world demonstrate that the quality of the inner spirit is not dependent upon them. The pastor considers that he is moving toward his goal when the patient says, "I can see now that what I need first of all is to view life from a Christian perspective. I will let these physical improvements follow if they will, but that is not my first objective." And there is a much better chance that such by-products *will* follow when they are not frantically sought after as chief goals.

THE PATIENT WHO OUGHT TO SEE A PSYCHIATRIST

What about the patient who is quite ill emotionally and really needs psychiatric treatment, but refuses it? Here the pastor may serve as a bridge to span the gap between medicine and psychiatry which is much too wide. In fact, it might be said that psychotherapy is in some respects closer to religion than it is to medicine. Even though psychiatry is a branch of medicine, its concerns are less with the body and more with the intangibles, like beliefs and feelings. The physician who practices psychotherapy exclusively is in some ways more a pastor than a physician, in the usual understanding of these titles.

Thus when a physician has a patient who resists seeing a psychiatrist, he may then suggest consulting a minister. He may even run into some resistance here. The patient may say, "Why should I see a minister? I'm not interested in religion"; or "I don't want to talk to one of those narrow-minded fellows." Whereupon the doctor might explain that because there is a close relationship between physical processes and the way a person looks at life, it is often helpful to talk to a minister. Getting a patient to see a minister also depends largely upon the physician's own enthusiasm about the particular minister he is recommending.

When the physician is quite certain that the patient will ultimately require psychiatric help, he indicates this to the minister so that the pastoral conversations can serve as a prelude to the psychiatrist's work. The pastor will then try to give the patient ample opportunity to talk freely about anything that concerns him. The patient will undoubtedly bring up his anxiety about psychiatry. If he is religious he usually worries about what psychiatry will do to his faith, particularly if he is familiar with Freud's statement that religion is a mass neurosis. The minister accepts this anxiety but explains that as he works closely with certain psychiatrists he finds that they have a deep respect for religion when it is not used neurotically. He may choose in some instances to say that he has also discovered in them a growing appreciation of spiritual values. This information may come as a blow to many patients who hope to use the minister as further defense against dealing with their problems in depth. Most of these patients sense that they need psychiatric help, but fear of the possible removal of their neurotic crutches causes them to go to any extreme to avoid it.

As these patients discover that their conversations with the minister are not too threatening to their security, they begin to inquire about the methods used by psychiatrists. When it is explained that psychotherapy is very similar to talking with a minister—that they are free to say or withhold whatever they choose—the next step, the referral, is not too difficult. The first appointment is usually made by phone in the patient's presence so that he can hear exactly what is said to the psychiatrist concerning him. The ordeal of making an appointment, when handled by his friend the minister, does not seem quite so dreadful as he had anticipated. He understands now that emotional upsets happen to many people.

The skillful minister is able to show patients rather quickly why they need specialized help. How and when to make a referral is one of the first things taught in clinical training. At the same time that the minister shows the patient his need for psychiatric care, he does not reject him, nor minimize the strength which can be found in religious faith. He offers to see the patient at regular intervals while he is in therapy. If the patient is afraid of losing his faith in the psychotherapeutic process, he can be assured that what is "lost" is usually an immature concept of God which needed to be discarded. The minister would be the first to encourage such a thorough examination of religious beliefs, although the psychiatrist may go at it differently.

What is to be done about patients who are not ill enough to go to a mental hospital and yet, because of the scarcity of psychiatrists, receive no care at all? Some clinically trained pastors, who

are willing to tackle more complex emotional problems, carry
on a kind of holding operation in close co-operation with a psychiatrist. The psychiatrist sees the patient once or twice and
agrees to continue as a consultant. The pastor then gives supportive therapy which may keep the patient from getting worse.
Some patients are helped considerably by this kind of care.

PATIENTS NOT IN NEED OF PSYCHOTHERAPY

Why is it that more and more ministers are willing to offer
their services to doctors in working with certain types of patients, particularly those who are *not* in need of a psychiatrist?
Not all ministers enjoy counseling, but a growing number prefer
it to the tremendous amount of parish administrative details
heaped on them. Many of them know that their abilities do not
lie along business or promotional lines, and they would rather
have these tasks taken over by capable laymen. Clergymen who
have gone into the ministry because of a desire to work with
people on an individual basis respond eagerly to the opportunity
to work with sick people for whom pastoral care may be the
right prescription.

Not all pastors are able to counsel, and the doctor will soon
discover which ones are the "naturals." When a pastor is found
to have this gift, he should be encouraged by doctors or members
of his congregation to take short refresher courses now available
at a number of seminaries and medical centers throughout the
country. The minister who keeps up-to-date on the latest developments will make professional co-operation much more feasible.
The clinical instruction he receives in these medical centers is
given in closest relation to medical people, so the student learns
how to work harmoniously with a wide variety of physicians.

Some congregations are adding more lay staff members to their
churches so the pastor can spend a greater part of his time giving
pastoral care to the increasing number of people referred by
physicians. Other congregations are putting an additional pastor
on the staff for the counseling and hospital ministry. There is a
growing appreciation of the need for closest co-operation between

churches and hospitals, just as between ministers and doctors. And these congregations are giving their counseling services free to the entire community, not just to church members. The cost of such a program is usually borne at the start by a few interested members of the church, but within a few years it usually becomes a regular item on the church budget.

CHAPTER 15

A Clergyman's Views on Psychiatry

As doctors and ministers work together they frequently must make decisions regarding the referral of a patient to a psychiatrist. Doctors often ask hospital chaplains what the general attitude of Protestant ministers is toward psychiatry, particularly psychotherapy. Without attempting to go into too much detail regarding the specific points of agreement or disagreement between Christian doctrine and psychiatric theory, I will try to give some of my impressions of the clergyman's reaction to psychiatry. Clearly, I cannot claim to express the opinion of clergymen in general, but the following impressions have grown out of my contact with hundreds of clergymen with whom I have worked in seminars and conferences across the country. When I use the word "psychiatry" in this chapter I will be referring to the whole area of dynamic psychology as represented by psychotherapists of many different "schools" and in particular those *medically* trained psychotherapists whose practice consists chiefly of talking with people.

It is no secret that clergymen have been both irritated and intrigued by the developments in the field of psychiatry. In the 1930's and 1940's pastors were irritated because some of the representatives of this new field made such extravagant claims for it and gave the impression that all their findings about the nature of man were unknown prior to Freud. But clergymen were intrigued by psychiatry's unusual ability to get behind the façade of man to the real person inside. Psychiatry's particular contribution lay in its description of the significance of the dynamic dimensions of the unconscious mind as it affects conscious behavior. Psychiatry says that when a man "makes up his mind" more than conscious processes are involved. Now we recognize the power of this dynamic unconscious, made up as it is of the sum total of experiences of a person, to influence all choices men make. These new descriptions of the unconscious remind us of the point so often made in Scripture concerning the complexity and depth of the human personality. The analytical study of human personality has helped clergymen to understand somewhat scientifically what the more sensitive religious leaders through the centuries had perceived intuitively.

In the 1930's a typical parish minister was quite naturally irritated by psychiatry when one of his church members, who was being treated by a psychiatrist, said that since he had gone into analysis, he had come to the realization that his religious beliefs were very superficial and he was considering giving up religion for something that would be more helpful. When he went on to describe his beliefs as having been "superimposed" upon him by his parents and other religious people, it took a very secure pastor to be able to admit that no doubt there was truth in what this man was saying. Perhaps this patient, and many other church members like him, *had* merely parroted religious statements, which they had never been helped to examine or make their own. The doctrines of the church had never "spoken" to them personally. If these doctrines really were the distillation of universal truth, growing out of the real experiences of man through the ages, then these doctrines should have helped to clarify the relevance of the Christian faith to personal living. Instead, these doctrines seemed so unrelated to life that people kept their religious "beliefs" in air-tight compartments where there was no chance for them to affect day-to-day decisions.

Many pastors met this scorching criticism of Christianity's failure to relate itself to life by opposing everything that psychiatrists said or did. But as the more thoughtful pastors began reflecting on what their parishioners were saying, they began to examine their own teaching and preaching and discovered that they had not made the Christian faith as relevant to life as they should. Gradually these pastors realized that many of their present church members *were* merely parroting what they were told to believe without ever having the opportunity to respond to or object to what they were being taught. As a growing number of pastors of a variety of denominations became sufficiently disturbed by psychiatry's criticism of religion's superficiality, they set about to re-evaluate the church's total educational program in an attempt to understand why the faith was not being integrated with life.

The rethinking process, then, has sought to relate the dynamic content of the Gospel to human experience. As a result of all this ferment, the curricula of many of the educational enterprises of the church have been or are now being carefully examined and revised. This rethinking has affected the educational philosophy of the Sunday School, the adult parish educational programs, as well as theological education itself.

Some psychiatrists were like the prophets of old in that they succeeded in disturbing the complacency of the church of their day. It is not difficult to understand why many clergymen became openly antagonistic to psychiatrists and took every opportunity to discourage their people from seeing them. But in spite of themselves, the clergy were stirred by the piercing, analytical explanations of human behavior appearing in the numerous articles written by psychiatrists. Much of this material made good sense, and it dealt with the very problems facing them in their own parishes. In fact, some ministers were struck by many of the similarities between psychotherapy and religious confessions. The difference was that these scientifically trained men were carefully reflecting upon what people were telling them and then attempting to postulate theories of human behavior. While some of the theories seemed absurd, the clergymen could not help but consider them. Psychiatrists were not objective in the criticisms they leveled against religion, but objective or not, there was much truth in what they said. Gradually small groups of parish pastors, who had been upset by psychiatry's criticisms, began to study more intensively the basic writings of Freud and others associated with the analytic movement. Before long these pastors were entering into fruitful discussions with psychiatrists.

As these ministers who made up little pockets of interest around the country became better acquainted with psychiatry, they sensed that many psychiatrists were engaged in what appeared to them to be fundamentally a religious work. Like themselves, psychiatrists were asking the basic questions related to the inner anxiety of man as he attempts to understand who he is and where he is going in a world which seems so reluctant to reveal her mysteries. Although psychiatrists received their training in a medical school, they were now stepping outside the usual bounds of medicine to ask whether health or absence of health could possibly be connected with the way a man looks at life. Certainly this question had significant religious implications.

One student has compared psychiatrists to those members of the medieval clergy who left the secular orders to go into monastic groups because they felt the need for a new approach to religion that would make it more vital in their day. Perhaps it could be said that psychiatrists broke away from the traditional patterns of medical practice so that they might wrestle with some of the underlying causes of illness. It is important to note that just as the monks remained within the framework of the church, so psychiatrists were still working within the framework of medicine. As ministers viewed this stirring within medicine and saw how it influenced other branches of medicine, they wondered whether a similar stirring in theology, aimed at exploring the underlying causes of spiritual difficulties, might have a telling effect upon the church's ministry. They began to turn the "analytic" spotlight on themselves. It revealed that the average minister was spending so much time in administrative work that he could not give his people the personal attention needed to make the Christian faith vital in their lives.

Amazingly enough, an unusually large number of ministers were soon admitting that the criticism by their people of their default in pastoral care was justified. These ministers invited psychiatrists to address them on a variety of subjects related to the pastoral care of people in distress and even encouraged them to be frank in pointing out the ministers' shortcomings. And most psychiatrists were not at all reluctant to do this.

Why were these ministers willing to take this searing criticism? Perhaps it was because psychiatry became a live issue at about the same time that these ministers were experiencing some dissatisfaction with their own ministry. The concept of the minister as a "pulpit-pounding preacher" was repugnant to them. They were not as certain as were their predecessors that preaching was the best way to proclaim the Gospel. Even their friends in educational psychology had questioned whether the lecture method was the best way to get any idea across. These ministers had sensed that their own preaching was always more effective when it was closely linked with personal contacts with their people. And the people themselves were beginning to ask why the church placed so little emphasis on personal ministry to individuals. Many of these people craved an opportunity to counsel with someone about their religious life as it related to their family and vocational problems. But ministers were not prepared for this new kind of ministry and they knew it. This made them all the more grateful for the insights into the dynamics of human behavior received from psychiatrists.

One of the first really mature studies of the relationship of religion and psychiatry was written in 1950 by Professor David E. Roberts of Union Theological Seminary, New York. His book, entitled *Psychotherapy and the Christian View of Man,* is required reading in most seminaries. Roberts' approach is so unbiased and so profound in its treatment of religion and psychiatry that leaders in both fields have used the book as a guide for interprofessional discussions. Roberts presents the basic assumptions of each profession and then points out the similarities and differences. The differences are often more in terminology than in underlying assumptions. Such terms as "anxiety," "guilt," "confession," "acceptance," and "salvation" describe not only religious experience, but psychological phenomena as well. When the minister is able, as Roberts is, to describe these concepts in psychological language, they take on new interest for the psychiatrist. Now it is his turn to be intrigued. He wants to know more about this new approach to the doctrines of the Christian faith, for in his daily work he is constantly confronted by patients who express feelings of guilt or loss of faith, or concern over the meaninglessness of existence.

PARTICULAR AREAS OF ENRICHMENT

If a minister were asked to list some of the areas of his own ministry which have been enriched by his contact with psychiatrists and psychiatric theory, he would probably include a few of the following things:

1. *Psychiatry has caused the minister to reassess the value of conversation.* For so long the minister was under the impression that he was called primarily to "proclaim the Gospel," and by that he meant evangelizing through preaching. Consequently, he spent little time trying to understand what was going on inside the people who listened to these proclamations. As indicated elsewhere in this book, ministers are now developing a new appreciation of the great changes which can be brought about by conversation. They see such conversations as having a sacred quality about them.

2. *Psychiatry has helped the minister to analyze the religious conversion experience.* Prior to psychiatry's probing approach it was thought to be sacrilegious for a clergyman to attempt to understand the psychological motivation involved in a person's response to the Christian message. In the past a young clergyman began his ministry with almost no theoretical understanding of the dynamics of human behavior. His ministry to people was by trial and error, and he was never sure why one approach worked with some people and did not work with others. He simply had to develop his intuitive sense as he grew older. Now the psychological dynamics of religious conversion are taught in most seminaries so that the student will be helped to recognize what is

taking place within the individual. While there is always an element of mystery about religious conversion, there are yet other aspects of it which are similar to the "reorientation" of character that takes place in psychotherapy.

Many Christian people assume that a religious conversion experience defies all psychological explanation. A conversion, they say, is an instantaneous event resulting in a complete change in a man's life. Now it is realized that there were a number of earlier experiences leading up to, and preparing the person for, the "moment of decision." The person undergoing a conversion experience has usually been dissatisfied with himself for a long time. Finally in such a climactic experience he is profoundly moved to make a dramatic "about face." In the "healthy conversion" the person has to come to himself in an uncoerced manner, even though outer forces may have helped trigger the final decision. When the minister understands the dynamics of this transforming event, he is in a better position to give the converted person the kind of pastoral care needed to reinforce a decision probably made in a moment of great emotion.

Although the psychiatrist does not use the term "conversion" in its religious sense to describe what happens in the psychotherapeutic reorientation of the person, there is much going on psychologically which resembles the prelude to a religious conversion. When a psychiatric patient, who has been morbid, cynical, or spiteful, begins to be more hopeful in the face of difficulties, enjoys making new friends, and goes out of his way to help those who need encouragement, then a kind of "conversion" experience has taken place, akin to the church's goal of being "born anew." To limit the work of God to the pastor's study is to say that God is not involved in the loving, concerned relationships which ideally, at least, develop between the professional psychotherapist and his patient. To be a channel of God's grace and love does not require a certificate of ordination.

3. *The minister appreciates that psychiatry has forced him to take a deeper look at the concept of sin.* There was a period in the 1920's when, in many churches, the word "sin" was scarcely men-

tioned. Someone said that sin returned with the coming of
dynamic psychiatry. One could not read a psychiatric case study
without being reminded that when a man is searchingly honest
with himself he cannot be very proud of what he finds within.
Psychiatrists did not label these malicious thoughts and deeds
"sins," but anyone reading the reports could soon tell that these
factors in a person's life were harmful and destructive.

Psychiatry has actually broadened the understanding of why
people sin. There is a slightly better idea why some people hang
on to a harmful habit or sin even though intellectually they are
fully aware that it will be their undoing. Or it has helped in
understanding why another person may never overcome his particular problems until some faulty defense mechanism, left over
from childhood, is rooted out. And now it is realized that when a
person is helped to understand the basic causes of his mental disturbance, he is at least on his way toward being cured.

4. *The minister sees that there is more to psychotherapy than
self-awareness.* However, for a time psychiatry gave the impression that a complete cure could be brought about simply by
developing self-awareness. Now it is known that clearing away
the neurotic overlay constitutes *only the beginning* of a long and
difficult process of reconstruction. And most psychiatrists recognize that while psychotherapy can penetrate deep into the unconscious and discover previously hidden motivations, this too constitutes only the beginning of the process, for even self-awareness,
when it is not harnessed to high ideals, is impotent to bring about
a change in the patient. One psychiatrist, Dr. Orville S. Walters,
points out that it is at this point that the minister must see his
peculiar responsibility. He says, ". . . but these usual objectives of
the professional psychotherapist are only incidental to the primary
objective of the minister. His task is to set the whole life of the
troubled individual in a Christian context and help him discover
the healing power of divine love—agape—in human and human-
divine relationships. . . . Psychological skill cannot bypass the basic
issue in human existence, whether men will accept reconciliation
with God through Christ, subordinating his own self-will and sin

to the inward reign of divine love. . . . Psychology, at once pene-
trating and impotent, may thus help to lay bare a problem that
only God's grace and man's commitment can resolve."*

5. *Psychiatry has taught the minister to have a new respect for
the importance of "feelings" as people make their day-to-day
decisions.* That is to say, in making all daily decisions people are
just as dependent upon their feelings or emotions as they are upon
their intellect. For a time in religious circles an effort was made
to divorce religion from feelings and emotions. Ministers had seen
what happened in the emotional excesses of a previous generation,
and they wanted modern man to make his religious commitment
free from emotional coercion. This is, of course, not only quite
impossible, but also undesirable, for the greatest achievements of
man occur when he is emotionally stirred to do something about
a particular situation. There is no longer need to insist that high
religion appeals only to the intellect. As religious educators take
emotions more into account they understand that if the church
would inspire a child or an adult to make a lifetime commitment
to the Christian faith, he will do so only if he is moved by his
deepest emotions. Religion, if it is devoid of emotional content,
can be taught, but not caught. To inspire a man to commit his
life to something requires more than intellectual assent. The minister must always be cognizant of the conflicting emotional drives
which make full religious commitment so difficult.

6. *Psychiatry has given the minister additional tools to help
him distinguish between a faith that is genuine and one that is
false.* No longer is the minister so easily taken in by people who
are using religion for their own purposes. Because of his new
insight into hidden motivations, he knows better how to minister
to the traditional church hypocrite who basically is a very unhappy person. But the minister, rather than thinking of this
person as a "public enemy," now seems him as someone who
needs help in understanding why he uses religion as he does. The
minister's task is to assist him in differentiating between real and
false security and then to provide strong supportive care and

* *Pastoral Psychology Magazine*, September, 1959. p. 53.

counseling during those months when he is trying to learn how to get along without the help of the neurotic crutches on which he has leaned.

7. *The minister—and in some sense, the whole Protestant church —has been smoked out by psychiatry regarding his views on sex.* While in 1930 there were almost no books available describing the church's attitude toward sex, today there are a score of excellent works by serious theologians written to aid in understanding the church's position.

Protestant ministers are speaking more freely in pulpits and in discussion groups concerning preparation for marriage—which includes the spiritual aspects of physical relationships. They are stating that the Bible has an essentially positive attitude toward sex and regards it as being given to man as a divine blessing to be enjoyed, not a curse to be escaped. However, the Bible also unmistakably takes man to task whenever he misuses his sexual potential by engaging in relationships unrelated to a mature expression of love.

The Rev. William G. Cole in his book *Sex in Christianity and Psychoanalysis* develops the thesis that the Hebrew tradition, and even Jesus himself, had a healthy naturalistic concept of sex. Dr. Cole believes that as the early Christians became less Jewish in their heritage and language, the Hellenistic concept of dualism took over. Increasingly, Christians developed the idea that it was virtuous to remain unmarried and that marriage was only a concession to the weak because sex was an evil necessity for the propagation of the race to be avoided and denied by the spiritually strong. Dr. Cole feels that the Apostle Paul "unwittingly played into this point of view as the anti-Hebrew exegetes interpreted his writings with a Hellenistic flavor. Paul was, however, essentially a Jew, a brother and kinsman to Jesus of Nazareth."

Ministers are now emphasizing that sex is not to be thought of only in terms of physical relations. Professor Seward Hiltner of the University of Chicago, in his reply to Dr. Kinsey in *Sex Ethics and the Kinsey Report*,* says, "Sex is, at root, a mystery. It is a

* New York: Association Press, 1953, p. 30.

mystery because it is a gift of God, always pointing beyond itself, operating through what appears to be mere biology toward the revelation of our nature as total personal spirit. We expect it to mean merely one thing; but when it fulfills its function, we know it has somehow gone beyond what we anticipated." To create such an attitude in the adult, it is necessary that he be conditioned as a child by a reverent appreciation of the body as the creation of God, without the restrictive ideas of shame and guilt which in the past have too often accompanied any mention of the body. Hiltner goes on to say, "Sex is too often equated with sin. But sex is no more nor less sinful than other areas of human activity. However, because it impinges on so many aspects of the human personality, it may appear to be more sinful than most other realms of human activity. When sex plays too important a role in the lives of people, it always stands in danger of becoming an idolatrous thing and eventually a substitute for God."

8. *Psychiatry has touched off a new appreciation of private confession.* Clergymen are considering the possibility of augmenting the usual prayer of confession in the worship service with the announcement of the availability of the pastor to talk with people privately.

In the Protestant pattern of church life it is very difficult for people to confess their sins in any specific manner. If they want to sing praises to God, or listen to a sermon, or engage in a multitude of Christian activities, the Protestant church can take care of them. But when it comes to wanting to admit some sinful thoughts or acts to another human being in order to hear from his lips the assurance that God does forgive those who are truly penitent, it is quite another thing.

Since so many people with neuroses and psychoses have complained to their psychiatrists, "It is impossible to talk to my minister about this," the church is seriously concerned about the absence of regular opportunity for private confession.

It is generally agreed, then, that clergymen have been stimulated to minister to the personal needs of their parishioners by the fructifying clinical research going on in psychiatry. Not only are parish pastors engaging in fairly regular contacts with psychiatrists in their communities, but theological professors are now inviting outstanding psychiatrists to engage in "high level talks" concerning the undergirding theory of both pastoral care and psychiatry. The next decade or two should prove very exciting as these two professions pool their resources on what they have learned about the nature of man.

PART IV

Areas of Joint Concern
for the Minister and Doctor

CHAPTER 16

Minister and Doctor Join to Strengthen Family Life

The minister and the doctor find it physically impossible to make as many house calls as formerly and still help those who come to their offices. This does not mean they are less concerned about the family. In fact, they have a growing appreciation of the importance of the home where basic ideas are formed relating to one's religion, one's concept of the meaning of health, and one's attitude toward life.

Some ministers who strive to call in every home in their parish once every year report that this requires them to drive up to twenty thousand miles annually. Using simple arithmetic, twenty thousand miles at an average of twenty-five miles an hour means the driver must be at the wheel of his car eight hours a day for about three months out of every year. This is a questionable expenditure of time and energy, to say the least. One reason for making house calls is to get acquainted with a family in its own particular setting and to gain some insight into how the family members react to one another. But even when the minister finds the entire family at home, which is very rare, these calls tend to become more social than pastoral. The minister wonders whether he is justified in using his particular training and talents in this way. He is more than willing to call in a home for some good pastoral reason, but he believes that in most cases he can better serve in strengthening the family by dealing with each member individually.

At this point it is well to consider the advice being given senior theological students regarding the encouragement of one-to-one conversations. It is suggested that when young pastors receive a class of new members into their church, they indicate to these people that they would like to set aside a half hour a year for a pastoral conversation with each of them. The purpose of this half hour is to make sure that the minister continues to have a personal acquaintance with each of these new members. Ministers often become so busy going out to gather another class of new members that they fail to deepen their relation with those who have already joined the church. New members are very pleased to find that they have joined a church where the minister actually has time for each member and treats each one as an individual.

This half-hour conversation is focused on the question, "What has it meant to you this past year to be a member of this Christian congregation?" And the pastor wants to know whether this church has really been serving the spiritual needs of this parishioner. Gradually, as the young pastor makes it a habit to set aside a half hour a year for each person, his study becomes a place of sacred memory for many people. It is through such pastoral conversations that he can feel the pulse of his congregation and deal with problems before they become too big to handle. Thus preventive pastoral care is similar to preventive medicine. A large percentage of these conversations move easily toward a discussion of what the person perceives to be a "rich, full life" and whether his goal is toward a kind of wholeness and health which has both physical and religious dimensions. And as the person talks about himself, the minister often recognizes the need to collaborate with the parishioner's doctor in dealing with the kinds of problems he presents.

Now to return to the theme of this chapter and some brief illustrations of the way in which ministers and doctors can work together toward the strengthening of the modern family.

During the past twenty-five years in a number of communities across the country, ministers and doctors have been engaged in interesting experiments in jointly attacking family problems. Prevention of problems before they become unmanageable was found to be the best approach, and the three groups with whom they have had the most success are (1) teen-agers, (2) engaged couples who are about to be married, and (3) married couples' clubs—primarily those related to churches. When a minister and a doctor jointly lead a discussion with any of these three groups, what are some of the subjects they cover and why are these groups the natural ones with which to consider ways to strengthen the family? For the purposes of this book the three groups will be classified under the general title "Education for Marriage."

1. *Education for marriage—with teen-agers.* The true preparation for strong family life begins in the home as the child learns from his father and mother how they deal with day-to-day problems. But there comes a time, perhaps during high school age, when some of the principles underlying solid family living need to be articulated so that youth will have some basis for making an independent choice of mates. When high schools and churches first began such discussions for their youth, the doctor was called in to discuss only "sex" or physiology of growth. The minister was called in to talk only about the "spiritual" aspects of preparation for marriage. This tended to give youth the impression that the physical and the spiritual aspects of family life can be separated. Undoubtedly, the most profitable discussions of the interrelation of these two aspects of life require the presence of both a minister and a doctor.

A much stronger impression of the family in its totality is left upon teen-agers when they listen to the interchange between the minister and the doctor. They are often surprised to find that the doctor talks quite naturally about spiritual matters and the minister is at ease in discussing physical aspects of growing up. Such joint leadership serves as a subtle way to protest against the usual compartmentalization of life.

A minister is fortunate if he has one or two doctors in his congregation who are willing to assist him with certain phases of the educational program. Particularly is this true with the topic of family life and the causes of instability therein. Teen-agers tend to be skeptical of what their parents say and even of what the minister says. On the other hand, they know that the doctor is exposed to every aspect of family life, and therefore what he says carries tremendous weight with them. These young people may appear blasé, but beneath this exterior is an earnest desire to have their questions taken seriously by someone who in their eyes has status. If a doctor can possibly take time to lead several discussions a year with teen-agers, he will be contributing immeasurably toward the building of healthy attitudes that lead to wholesome living. Community service of this kind is in the best tradition of preventive medicine. It is as important for the doctor to give his services in this way as it is for him to devote some time to teach in the nearby medical school.

Perhaps teen-agers are the most difficult group to work with and yet the experience can be extremely rewarding. I can remember my own high school days when Coach Alonzo Stagg of the University of Chicago spoke to our Hi-Y organization on the subject of "clean sportsmanship." Following his speech there were so many questions of a semi-medical nature that he decided to bring a doctor with him at the next meeting. The fact that several of us can still vividly remember the interchange between the coach and the doctor in response to our questions indicates the subject must have been of great importance to all of us. It is one of the reasons why I continue to encourage ministers to invite doctors to join with them in leading discussion groups.

2. *Education for marriage—with engaged couples.* Doctors are playing an increasingly important role in education for marriage courses across the country. There are two basic patterns which these discussion groups follow: (a) A full evening for couples about to be married, devoted to lectures and discussion on the physical and spiritual aspects of marriage. This complete-in-one-evening course is held in a church, YMCA, or hospital and is conducted jointly by a minister and a doctor. (b) Four two-hour periods held on Sunday afternoons or weekday evenings in which each of four topics is given two full hours for discussion. The topics concern the physical, spiritual, psychological, and economic aspects of marriage. The co-ordinator, usually a clergymen, pro-

vides a synthesis of the various approaches. A doctor, a psychiatrist, and a lawyer or economist share leadership of the group.

These courses are usually held under the sponsorship of several churches because there are not enough marriages in one church to warrant a regular series of discussions throughout the year. Often the several churches work with the county medical society in arranging leaders for the meetings, and thus the program receives the backing of all the ministers and doctors of the county. General announcements are made in the newspapers from time to time reminding all couples contemplating marriage to enroll in the education for marriage course. Some churches require that each couple attend the course before the marriage can be solemnized.

Ministers once assumed wrongly that couples would not be willing to attend courses in preparation for marriage. In areas where such courses are well publicized couples are getting in touch with their minister well ahead of the contemplated date of their marriage so that they can participate in the instructions. Most couples enter marriage with real seriousness, and the seemingly shabby preparation for marriage in the past has been primarily the fault of those who performed the ceremony, not the fault of the couples.

It is impossible in the pages of this book to examine more than just a few areas of discussion in which the minister and doctor are jointly concerned. I will, however, touch on four controversial subjects—birth control or responsible parenthood, sex education, sterilization, and artificial insemination. The first two will be considered in some detail so as to illustrate the general method of presenting other topics. Birth control will be discussed somewhat as it is presented to couples about to be married, and sex education for children as it is discussed with married couples groups. If the reader is interested in a more detailed study of the major topics covered at a four-session education for marriage course, he may obtain a mimeographed manual published by Planned Parenthood Association of Chicago. It contains the essential parts of the lecture-discussion conducted by the clergyman, doctor, psychiatrist, and economist.

Birth control, or what is often called responsible parenthood, is a subject of particular interest to the minister and the doctor, for parishioners and patients are asking many questions about the moral and medical aspects of family planning. The Protestant church has been rethinking its position on this problem. Or perhaps it should be said that for the first time Protestant denominations are defining their position publicly. It is impossible to speak for every denomination, but the majority of Protestant people are probably spoken for in the following comments about birth control.

Birth control, sometimes referred to by Protestants as "conception control," means that a husband and wife should feel a sense of responsibility for every child they bring into the world. Or to put it another way, now that there are medically approved methods of preventing unplanned births, every child has the right to be wanted, loved, and amply provided with the physical and spiritual necessities of life. This is why Protestants prefer to speak of birth control as *responsible parenthood*.

In discussions with engaged couples the minister and the doctor occasionally learn that although the couple ultimately desire a family, they plan to use birth control methods for "a few years" because they both want to work. The minister and the doctor ought to emphasize that too much delay might hinder the maturing process in marriage. The one great danger to be guarded against when advocating birth control is that people may be tempted to use it for selfish purposes. The couple who before having their first baby want to have some money in the bank, or drive the latest car, or own their own home, or take expensive vacations, are people who may be using the blessing of birth control to their own detriment. As they live together, unhampered by the normal, daily demands of a child, they build a little wall around themselves which tends to isolate them from the realities of family living. Each year that they keep from having a child for selfish purposes, the wall gets a bit higher and thicker. When several years have passed and they finally decide that it is now or never, the youngster is born into a somewhat abnormal environment.

Another reason for encouraging couples to have their children as soon after marriage as is feasible grows out of experience with childless couples who are now in their middle thirties and have come to a fertility clinic for help because they are unable to have children. One fairly typical wife of thirty-four who had been married ten years was asked by the doctor how long they had been trying to have a family. She replied, "For the last three years." But what about the first seven years?" the doctor asked. "Oh, we were both working and I had a good job." It is important that couples should find out early whether or not they can have a family. In this way, they can still get the maximum help from fertility clinics and, failing in this, they can make their application at an adoptive agency well before they reach the age of thirty-five or forty when most agencies automatically drop them. Even when there is a good possibility of obtaining a child, the waiting period is usually two or more years. Some couples are so determined to adopt a child that they move to a different part of the country where agencies have children available for adoption. But even such an effort has often been without success.

It is important, therefore, to encourage couples to begin trying to have a family at the earliest possible time for the reasons given, and also because the peak of fertility in the average wife is reached about the age of twenty-eight, and the chances of conception actually decrease with each passing year.

Having said all this, the church encourages birth control practices when any of the following reasons are present:

For the purpose of personal adjustment. Some couples would like to have their first child right away. Most couples, however, would like to enjoy being "bride and groom" for a few months without the discomforts and embarrassment of nausea and morning sickness, and friends saying, "Couldn't they wait even a month?" Particularly a couple having known each other for less than a year prior to the wedding find the first months of marriage but a continuation, on a deeper level, of their courtship. Many of the rough edges, which normally are smoothed off in the less charged atmosphere of "dating," now have to be handled within the four walls of the new home without the advantage of "cooling off" periods which in courtship take place between dates. It seems unfair to add the additional factor of pregnancy to the usual tensions of the first year of adjustment. The length of the adjustment period is usually six months to about a year and a half.

For the purpose of spacing children. Again it must be realized that some couples would like to have all their children in a row— one every strawberry season. But most young mothers would like to have a breathing period between the coming of each child so that they can get back on their feet and get the household routine under control. It is so much better to hear a mother say, "Bill and I can hardly wait until this next baby comes," rather than, "I hate to admit it, but I'm pregnant again, and I'm just not up to having another child right now." Underlying the Protestant emphasis on responsible parenthood is the recognition that every child has the right to be welcomed enthusiastically into his new home. His parents demonstrate their own maturity by taking the necessary medically approved precautions so that a child comes to them as the result of planning, not just passion. How often one sees the results of uncontrolled physical emotion within marriage where children are brought into the world unwanted and unloved. The church, therefore, encourages parents to utilize the blessings of medical discoveries about contraception which do not minimize the joys of sexual union. It is hoped that soon conception control will be more generally used in countries like India and China to forestall the condemnation of future generations to a groveling and subhuman existence.

For health or economic reasons. Some couples at a particular time in their lives are not in a physical or economic condition to have children. Where a doctor on medical grounds cautions against having children for a certain period of time or where it is obvious to the couple that economically they cannot afford another child, then birth control methods are certainly in order.

For those whose families have reached a maximum size. Suppose a husband and wife are both thirty-three years old. They have been married ten years and have four children, for them the ideal size for a family. With the usual amount of parental sacrifice they can adequately provide for these four children and see to it that they have a good education. It seems only right and Christian that this couple should now be able to put all their energy into being the right kind of parents to these four children. The inner happiness and security which these parents radiate can be further enhanced if they can continue to be together as man and wife without the worries and anxieties of possible pregnancies. The church would be the first to object to contraception when used for selfish or degrading purposes either in marriage or outside of it. But when a family has reached its maximum size, the parents should not be kept apart physically when the fear of pregnancy can now be removed by medically approved methods.

It would be quite another matter to suggest tying the tubes in the female or performing a vasectomy in the male. Such a permanent procedure requires an entirely different approach to the problem. Present birth-control methods—the condom, diaphragm, and specially approved jellies—do not deprive parents of the power of reproducing should they change their minds. The death of children or of a parent and subsequent remarriage all may make it desirable to have more children.

METHODS OF BIRTH CONTROL

Total abstinence. This method is not approved by most Protestants because it keeps husbands and wives apart unnecessarily. God has so made us that when "the two become one flesh" in holy matrimony, there is a blending of the whole man and the whole woman which is symbolized and brought to its most intimate moment in the physical relationship. We apparently are the only ones of God's creatures who face each other in the act of intercourse. At least we are the only ones for whom the act can become a spiritual experience as well as a physical one. How then could anyone deny this exceptional God-given gift to humans by keeping a husband and wife apart simply because of the unnecessary fear of pregnancy?

It is understandable why the church leaders discouraged birth control before the discovery of harmless methods of contraception. Now it is gratifying that the National Council of the Churches of Christ in the U.S.A. through its various committees has studied every aspect of this problem and has published statements similar to the one given above. As one leader put it, "We surely would not hesitate to encourage the use of insulin for diabetes, or penicillin for pneumonia. Why then would we think of discouraging the use of medical discoveries in birth control for the purpose of keeping unwanted children from being born?"

Rhythm. This method is being used by an increasing number of couples as medical science is able to make rhythm more dependable. Formerly, rhythm was used by couples who did not mind if a "slip" occurred. Recent studies indicate that when the couple carefully follows the doctor's instructions, there is little likelihood of an unexpected pregnancy.

Medically approved methods of birth control include condom, diaphragm, and specially prepared jellies. Any of these when used as prescribed by a physician give the couple a maximum amount of security. It is the church's task, along with the medical profession, to train young people and married couples so that these methods will not be used for purposes that are degrading or selfish. Just as with atomic energy, leaders must work diligently to impress on people that these discoveries are for the good of mankind and not for its detriment.*

Education for marriage—with married couples. If the minister and doctor find it a rewarding experience to work with teenagers and with couples about to be married, they will find it even more rewarding to work with married couples. With teen-agers

---

* For further discussion of premarital counseling with engaged couples see the *Education for Marriage Course Manual* published by Planned Parenthood of Chicago and *Premarital Counseling* by Granger Westberg, published by the National Council of the Churches of Christ in the U.S.A.

and engaged couples many of the problems discussed are academic. With married couples the reverse is true.

Where the group is not too large—say about twenty people—and where leadership has not stifled free discussion, every member of the group eventually participates. There are always couples present who at that moment are wrestling with certain problems which they think are unique to them. Without admitting it aloud, they have wondered whether the only solution in their case is divorce. Then as they attend a meeting of other married couples led by a minister and a doctor in which many of their own personal problems are presented as of general concern to all, they relax from their tension. From then on they find that they can deal much more objectively with their own problems.

With most married couples' groups it is best not to start with personal problems. These people usually do not know one another well enough to dare say much in public. One way to begin is to focus the discussion on problems of raising children. Such problems bear a strong resemblance to the ones facing adults who are still acting like children. When a doctor is participating in the leadership of the group, a logical theme to begin with is "sex education for children." As stated earlier, education for marriage begins in the home; thus anything done along these lines for teen-agers and engaged couples is greatly influenced by what they have learned in their own homes as they have been growing up.

It seems only logical, then, that education for marriage really ought to begin with parents who still have small children. When parents meet with other parents under the leadership of a minister and a doctor, it helps immeasurably to accomplish the twofold task of deepening their concepts of Christian family life and hopefully their children's concepts also. Parents who participate in such a series of discussions make excellent students because they seriously attempt to try out what the teacher says in their own laboratory at home.

Now to take a look at that task which faces all parents—namely, answering their children's questions about sex. There is general agreement that sex education, because of the strong emotional and religious overtones, can best be given by parents to their own children. It is such a normal and natural part of growing up that children's questions ought to be answered by those who are closest to them at the time they arise. Schoolteachers also have to handle many of the questions that arise, and these discussions too should come about naturally in the context of courses dealing with anatomy, art, literature, etc. To have a special course on sex education is to put the subject in an unnatural setting.

Parents can be helped to learn how to talk to their children about the growth process and to relate this with God's plan for the continuation of life. It is one thing to give straight physical facts and quite another to tell the story in a way that shows how parents actually participate in the creative activity of God. The first is just information; the second is information that enriches a child's understanding of God and man's relationship to him.

It is the interpretation of sex information which is of particular concern today. Many more facts are being given to children now than at the turn of the century, but just knowing these facts is not the answer to the many problems in this area. It is desirable for children to understand the remarkable reproductive process as a feature of the miracle of life itself, a gift of God. When the child hears the physical aspects of human development presented in this light, sex takes on an entirely different character. It is much more than the story of animal mating.

If a doctor is willing to offer his services to a married couples' club, he can help these young parents to understand and to deal with the kinds of questions their children will be asking. The following paragraphs illustrate some of the many ways doctors have spoken to such groups.

WHAT THE DOCTOR SAYS TO YOUNG MARRIED COUPLES

As I have participated in a number of discussion groups I have jotted down many of the things which doctors say which I think are worth remembering.

Sex education begins when the child asks his first questions about the human body. Parents are encouraged to answer these questions at the time they are asked. The answers are given simply, without embellishment and without embarrassment. It is a good thing for the parents to practice using some of the medical and anatomical terms in their own conversation. Parents should be ready to handle the three basic questions which most children ask even before they go to kindergarten.

The first is, "Where do babies come from?" The best answer is the honest one. It might go something like this: "God has made a special place in the mommy's body near her heart where the little baby grows." Instead of "body" you might say "tummy" or "stomach." This is all there is to it except that the child may want to feel the mother's tummy, which certainly is not harmful.

The second question, which will come a little later—a few weeks or months—is, "I know that the baby is growing inside the mommy, but how is the baby going to get out?"

While a great many parents are doing a fairly good job with the first question, they are usually stopped by the second. How far should one go in giving details of birth to a child of five? The most important part of the answer, of course, is not what details are given, but *how* they are given. If the parent is relaxed and at ease, then the child will not dwell on this aspect of existence any more than on some other. But if the parent avoids the question or goes to the other extreme and gives an answer in great detail, then the child may sense that this is a conflictual area, and he reacts in any of a variety of unhealthy ways. The answer to this second question should be stated as simply as possible: "When the little baby has grown large enough to live by itself outside the mother's body, the baby comes out through a special opening God has made between the mother's legs."

It might not happen quite that easily, but for the child the accent is on the fact that God has made a *special* opening just for babies to come through. Some children respond by saying, "You mean the opening is down there where you go to the toilet?" And the reply is, "Yes, it is in the same general area, but it is not the same opening that you use for urination or for BMs. This is a special opening just for babies to come through." "But," says the child, "isn't it dirty down there?" "No," you say, "we wash those parts of the body just as you wash your neck and arms and feet." And by that time you are so exhausted from the ordeal, it is perfectly all right to change the subject.

We are not saying that this approach to sex education is easy to get on to. What we are saying is that in the long run it pays dividends because the child can handle the truth better than he can handle lies, deceit, and vagueness. For many reasons these three breed all sorts of strange ideas which have such a strong effect upon the child that they color his thinking in these areas the rest of his life. It is true that many emotional problems have their beginning in warped attitudes toward sex. So it is high time that leaders in religion and medicine set about to correct the problem where it can best be handled—by parents in the home. Twenty years from now we may have different and better ways of carrying on sex instruction, but when we look back, we will not have to apologize for our early, faltering steps. At least we will have been doing something about the ignorance which has caused so much harm to former generations, for we are convinced that truth about sex is more wholesome than vagueness or actual untruths.

Perhaps it should be said at this point that there are some children who never even ask the first two questions. Some parents are pleased at this because it saves them from having to face the problem. But experts are convinced that if a child does not ask the first two questions by the age of seven, the parents should then find out whether the child does know the answers. One of three things usually has taken place. He has gotten some answers from his playmates and these are usually incorrect or on a subverbal level; he has gotten the idea from his parents that these are questions which a child is not supposed to ask; or he may not have that kind of curiosity. But by age seven, we think he should know the answers to the first two normal questions. Furthermore, the answers should be given to him by his parents so that when further questions arise in the child's young life, he will know that he can always talk to his parents about these matters.

Now to come to the third question. The child may phrase it this way: "I know how the baby is going to get out of there, but how does the baby get into the mommy's tummy in the first place?" To the very young child, four to seven years of age, the details of sexual intercourse are not comprehensible and so nothing of this is mentioned in the answer. The parent only says, "When a mommy and a daddy decide to have a little baby, the daddy plants a seed in the mommy and this starts the baby growing. So you see it takes both a daddy and a mommy to have a baby." This answer usually suffices and is not emotionally disturbing to the child because the story of reproduction for him has never been related to off-color stories and experiences.

If the child is somewhat older and asks, "How does the daddy plant the seed?" the reply might be, "The daddy places his penis in the mommy's vagina and the sperm from the daddy then goes into the mommy and starts the baby." If the child persist and says, "I want to see you do it," the soft but firm answer could be "No, you will not get to see a baby started until you are a daddy or a mommy. Starting a baby is just for daddies and mommies because that's the way God has arranged it." Period. There can be no shabby or foolish talk at this point. The parent is dead serious about this. Yet it does not harm his relationship with the child to say "no" and mean it, for the parent has been truthful throughout the conversation. This the child can sense, and unless there is a basic weakness in the parent's attitude, the child will accept the firmness of the "no" as an indication of one of life's limitations. The child must learn what life is like. What better persons are there to teach him than his parents who at the same time that they reveal life's negative can surround him with love and tenderness?

What about the parents who answer the child's questions in somewhat the manner indicated here only to find that this upsets the neighbors because they do not believe in such "sex talk"? Formerly this reaction presented quite a problem, for there was no general agreement about such instruction. Today it is different. All one needs to say to such neighbors is, "Haven't you heard that all the churches—Protestant, Catholic, and Jewish—have agreed that it is the parent's *responsibility* to get this information across to the child in a natural and dignified setting *before* he gets to the playground where he will hear about it in a vulgar and even harmful manner?"

Our experience has been that people who react negatively to such "telling" are quite willing to rethink their point of view after hearing a discussion of the subject by a doctor and a minister. We stress the need to hear it from *both* professions because people have to be convinced that it is the right thing to do not only medically, but also that it is approved morally and spiritually.

Considerable space has been devoted here to comments on sex education and responsible parenthood because these might well be the first two topics assigned to a doctor who is willing to participate in group discussions. Doctors will undoubtedly also be asked to discuss sterilization and artificial insemination.

Sterilization. This subject will usually be brought up in the married couples' group when a mother who has had severe difficulty in bearing children receives medical advice warning that another pregnancy will endanger her life. The group will also probably want to talk about the reasons for sterilization. In preparation for such a discussion the reader is referred to the excellent book entitled *Morals and Medicine* by Professor Joseph Fletcher of Episcopal Theological Seminary, Cambridge, Massachusetts. Dr. Fletcher presents a very thorough analysis of the problems which sterilization raises when advocated for therapeutic, eugenic, or punitive reasons. Among other things he says that "we cannot escape from the conviction that it is a grave wrong and a betrayal of the Christian conception of personality, as well as against a rational conscience, to allow stunted and defective lives to be propagated when the means are available in medicine to prevent it. It would seem blasphemous to assert that God wills or purposes that defective children should be born.... Normal people are responsible, and that responsibility includes bringing new lives into the world."*

* Princeton University Press, 1954, pp. 164, 165.

Artificial insemination. While perhaps no married couple in the group will admit to a personal interest in this problem, and for obvious reasons, almost everyone is interested in the medical and moral questions it raises. In cases of incurable sterility in the husband where the doctor suggests that the couple consider artificial insemination, all kinds of doubts arise in the couple's minds concerning the rightness of this procedure. People often speak derogatively of artificial insemination as a kind of laboratory breeding of test-tube babies—breeding which they say is far more animal-like than human. Or people say it is a sin against the law of God since the sperm of the husband is not present. Or people say it is just plain adultery, and the children of such an arrangement are illegitimate.

Again I am indebted to Professor Fletcher for his incisive treatment of the subject. I will quote his provocative summary statement even though it is quite unfair to him not to include the cogent arguments which lead up to it. I do so in the hope that every reader will be sufficiently intrigued to want to read the entire book.

Dr. Fletcher says: "Insemination from a donor is not adultery if marriage fidelity is conceived, as our own principles require, to be a personal rather than a merely legal relationship. In the first place, artificial insemination mutually agreed upon by husband and wife does not involve any broken faith between them. In the second place, no personal relationship is entered into with the donor at all. On Christian grounds, in particular, to call artificial insemination with anonymous donor 'adultery' is to give it a quality different altogether from the one envisaged in the New Testament, where the highly personal nature of the sexual union is the thing confined to marriage partners." *

Religio-medical interests are so intertwined that it would be quite difficult if not impossible to try to present them separately. So many aspects of family life have this same kind of intermeshing of the physical and the spiritual that too much stress cannot be

* *Ibid.*, p. 121.

placed on the need for more and more joint enterprises between doctors and ministers.

Another important area of joint concern is faith healing. Again, as in the four topics of the present chapter, it is impossible to discuss faith healing in any depth at all without viewing it from both the medical and the theological perspective. This will be the aim of the next chapter.

CHAPTER 17

Faith Healing—A Problem for Doctors and Ministers

There is a revival of interest in faith healing in the United States and abroad. Faith healers were previously limited to audiences which could see them at work in their tents or rented auditoriums. The radio was not a good medium for them, but television, combining sight with sound, has increased their audiences tremendously. People who never would have entered a faith healer's tent are now unapologetically watching television presentations of this type which serve as a form of entertainment. They are not too different from the "give-away" shows, for everyone is anxious to see who is going to be lucky enough to be healed this time. A person with an incurable illness thinks that maybe "it would not hurt" to try faith healing.

Those who consider suggesting that a sick relative go to a faith healer often feel that they ought to talk it over first with their minister or doctor. Consequently, it is necessary to have some idea what faith healing is all about. For the most part, there is some confusion about faith healing because neither the church nor the medical profession has as yet gone to the trouble of separating fiction and fact. Because ministers and doctors are poorly informed, those who ask them questions go away feeling either that the latter are prejudiced against it or that they know little about it. They feel justified, therefore, in trying faith healing to see if it works.

The motives which bring people to faith healers are not necessarily religious. In many cases there is no real desire on the part of sick persons or their friends to draw closer to God. People often go to the faith healer for the same reason they go to a physician —they have heard that he is "good at curing people." But such healing is not seen in the context in which Christ put it; namely, a ministry to the whole man, which includes his spiritual as well as his physical needs. The faith healer has usually been considered a quack both by the church and by the medical profession. He practices neither good religion nor good medicine. Until recently he had been dismissed from the minds of ministers and doctors, for generally he touched only the fanatical fringe of the population. But now that he is influencing the thinking of their own patients and parishioners, and with the growing interest in faith healing by the people in the United States and abroad, ministers and doctors can no longer remain uninformed on this subject.

To express disinterest in faith healing or to imply that it is quackery often causes questioners to remark that throughout history it was always the "professional" people who opposed new ideas. Although there is objection to calling these *new* ideas, yet it is now required of leaders in the field of religion and health at least to recognize that there is such a phenomenon as healing brought about by nonmaterial means. It would be unfortunate if they refused to clarify the issues and thus encouraged people to follow the wrong kind of leaders in faith healing.

Faith healing should be the subject of a long-term research project undertaken by a group of outstanding medical scientists and clergymen and on which periodic reports will be written. The beginnings of such a project are being made by several denominations and their preliminary reports are now available.

It is to be hoped that there will also be a special study group composed of people representing all shades and expressions of religious belief and disbelief. It perhaps could be co-operatively sponsored by the American Medical Association, the American Psychological Association, and the National Council of the Churches of Christ in the U.S.A. The staff of researchers should include smaller inquiry committees which will investigate purported healings in all parts of the country. They would make a careful study of individual patients, medical records, and of the persons through whom the healing was brought about. Much can be learned at this point from the methods employed by the Roman Catholic Church in investigating purported miracles at Lourdes and at Ste. Anne de Beaupré. Scientists and searchers after the truth realize that this phenomenon has never been effectively investigated because of inadequate tools available for such study. However, the recent developments in psychiatry and psychology have provided a few of these necessary tools. Qualified scholars must give their best to the study and present clear and forthright statements and opinions based on careful investigation. Otherwise, it is possible that a rather large segment of the population will lose confidence in religion and medicine and will easily revert to primitive conceptions. According to anthropologists, modern man is not so modern; with a little encouragement he could bring back habits and customs based on magic and superstition. Thus a faith-healing movement lacking the guidance of the church and medicine could do a great deal of damage and actually dissipate the progress we have already made.

Despite all the questions that may arise about faith healers, they have challenged churches to take a new long look at the New Testament, a large part of which is devoted to the healing ministry of Christ. Churches today tend to skip over these healing miracles. They avoid the command of Christ to "go out and preach the gospel and heal the sick," and imply that this has all been taken care of by religion's interest in hospitals and nursing schools. They seldom come to grips with the question of whether Jesus really meant that his followers were to heal those who were sick in body as well as those who were sick in mind or spirit. The church knows that the early followers of Christ performed a great many healings, but eventually people were removed from the Great Healer, both in time and in quality of relationship, and this healing ability diminished. Today the church's interest in physical healing is related almost entirely to *materia medica* or the practice of scientific medicine.

Whenever the church, throughout its long history, has neglected some phase of the Christian Gospel, a sect has sprung up to fill the vacuum. In many cases the sect, though declared heretical, had a wholesome influence upon the church, for its members continued to "needle" the established church until she had to do something about the aspect of the Christian faith which she had been neglecting. In this age, Christian Science is the major group which has filled a vacuum and reminded the more orthodox church that it has forgotten to emphasize the healing ministry of the Gospel. Christian Science, however, has become so concerned about the faith-healing idea around which it grew, that many feel it has overemphasized healing almost to the exclusion of other aspects of the Christian message.

This is not the place to give a detailed account of the many objections to the tenets of Christian Science or of other groups which stress healing through faith. These groups are mentioned only to point out that the church must have been very negligent in its emphasis on the religious aspects of illness to cause so many thousands of its members to leave the church to affiliate with faith-healing groups. Today, instead of fighting such movements, the church's task is to study them carefully to learn what is so convincing about their doctrines and how these relate to the concept of health and healing in traditional Christian theology. If the core of what they say is basically Christian and worthy of being taught, then the church will have to rethink its approach to the problem of illness.

Not all faith healers are outside the established churches and not all are suspect. A small but quiet group of reputable Christians are at present exploring what they choose to call "spiritual healing," as contrasted with "faith healing." A few of them are good scholars and have written books which deserve a place in medical and theological libraries.* These writers believe that "God is on

* Wade H. Boggs, Jr., *Faith Healing and the Christian Faith* (Richmond: John Knox Press, 1956); A. Graham Ikin, *New Concepts of Healing* (New York: Association Press, 1956); Leslie D. Weatherhead, *Psychology, Religion and Healing* (Nashville: Abingdon Press, 1948).

the side of health," and that the normal state of man is to be healthy. They say that Christ demonstrated this by his evident distress at the sight of suffering or disease and his willingness to try to do something about it. When he ministered to people, it was always to the whole person, never to a soul unattached to a body. If the person to whom he was speaking was ill physically as well as spiritually, he set about to heal both. It is said that Christ was successful only if the person was willing to do his part by having sufficient faith to believe that the change could take place. It is quite clear, then, that Jesus sought to heal disease-filled bodies as well as sin-sick minds. Therefore, it was not out of character for him to commission his disciples to "preach the gospel and heal the sick." These students of spiritual healing believe, therefore, that when one proclaims the Christian message, one must always present both the teaching *and* the healing aspects of this message.

A second thesis of these interpreters of spiritual healing is that "God does not send disease" to anyone. They emphasize the fact that Christ cannot be pictured as one who inflicts disease. If it is believed that God is best described as "loving, merciful, and just," then for him to send disease would be contrary to his nature. They are concerned over people's belief that a person is ill because "it must be God's will," or that some unexplainable catastrophe or form of suffering "must be God's will." To believe this is humbly to admit an ignorance of the great mysteries of the universe, but actually people are saying two things at the same time. First, they say they do not understand the great mysteries of life, for these are all in the hands of a loving and merciful God. Yet at the same time they complain, though they do not admit it aloud, that they think a God who brings about or at least allows such suffering is a tyrant and a despot.

Now which of these two do people mean? Is God loving and merciful, or is he a capricious tyrant? He cannot be both. This is what confuses them, for they are not clear as to what they believe about the nature of God. Leslie Weatherhead, the well-known British divine, gives the following two illustrations which point up the dilemma. They are found in his excellent little book

entitled *The Will of God** which might well be on the reading
list of every doctor and minister.

Dr. Weatherhead says, "The phrase 'the will of God' is used
so loosely and the consequence of that looseness to our peace of
mind is serious. . . . Let me illustrate the confusion. I have a good
friend whose dearly loved wife recently died. When she was
dead, he said, 'Well, I must just accept it. It is the will of God.'
But he himself is a doctor and for weeks he had been fighting for
her life. He had called in the best specialists in London. He had
used all the devices of modern science, all the inventive apparatus
by which the energies of nature can be used to fight disease. Was
he all that time fighting *against* the will of God? If she had recov-
ered, would he not have called her recovery the will of God? Yet
surely we cannot have it both ways."

Another illustration from Weatherhead is particularly poignant:
"I was standing on the veranda of a home in India darkened by
bereavement. My Indian friend had lost his little son, the light of
his eyes, in a cholera epidemic. At the far end of the veranda his
little daughter, the only remaining child, slept in a cot covered
over with a mosquito net. We paced up and down and I tried in
my clumsy way to comfort and console him. But he said, 'Well,
padre, it is the will of God.' Fortunately I knew him well enough
to be able to reply without being misunderstood and I said something like this: 'Supposing someone crept up the steps onto the
veranda tonight while you all slept, and deliberately put a wad of
cotton soaked in cholera germ culture over your little girl's
mouth. What would you think about that?'

" 'My God,' he said, 'what would I think about that? Nobody
would do such a damnable thing. What do you mean by suggesting such a thing?' 'But John,' I said, 'isn't that just what you have
accused God of doing when you said it was His will?' "

These two illustrations indicate the need for ministers and
doctors to do some homework in trying to understand how such
a concept of God applies to the many problems of sickness and
health faced in their daily rounds in the hospital and the parish.

* Nashville: Abingdon Press, 1944.

Among members of the established denominations in America there is a growing interest in describing what the church does in its *total* pastoral care of people as "a healing ministry." There is fairly general agreement that the church's ministry can be quite fully and succinctly stated in the general commission of Christ to "preach and heal." In this context "heal" includes much more than just physical healing. It means to care enough about people to recognize their need for healing of whatever type—social, spiritual, mental, physical—and bring to these persons the healing balm of the "concerned community of Christians" who represent, however feebly, the concerned Father of all.

When the word "heal" is considered in the context of the practicing physician, the statement by the Swiss physician Dr. Paul Tournier comes to mind:* "The doctor's first task is to heal. In some cases measures of a technical nature only are needed. But with many patients the doctor's task can only be fulfilled by his accepting a wider mission, an educative one. He is called upon to help people to develop, to re-enter the main stream of life by conforming to the laws of life, to grow up harmoniously, to become adult. This is in any case the true aim of technical medicine also; the removal of every physical and psychical obstacle to growth and development of the person, so that its purpose in life may be accomplished."

Both the pastor and the physician need to be reminded of the twofold nature of their task—to educate (or preach) and to heal.

It is clear that the many problems raised by the faith-healing movement will not soon be settled. It is incumbent upon all who are in the healing professions to approach this matter of faith healing with openness and a willingness to change their present opinions if necessary. All studies of faith-healing phenomena should be carried on with as much scientific objectivity as is possible in so controversial an area. It will be necessary to compare each faith healer's point of view with that of Christ who is the norm. Christ evidenced a particular spirit as he went about preaching and healing. His healing was always *incidental* to his

* *The Meaning of Persons* (New York: Harper & Brothers, 1957), p. 200.

preaching, and on more than one occasion he asked the person whom he helped to "tell no man." Jesus was always concerned lest the miracle get in the way of the message. There will therefore be serious doubts about the validity of any present-day faith healing which maximizes physical healing and minimizes the inner spiritual change so necessary to the Christian concept of health.

CHAPTER 18

Action Research in Interprofessional Co-operation
The Kokomo Project

Throughout this book I have sought to point up some of the ways physicians and clergymen might work together for the benefit of the people they serve. In this final chapter I will describe the early stages of an ongoing action research project in Kokomo, Indiana, in which there has been more success than expected in engaging almost all the full-time clergymen of the city of Kokomo and of Howard County in making a start in implementing some of the suggestions made in this book.

The Kokomo project grew out of one of the University of Chicago's regular two-week seminars for parish pastors on the subject of pastoral counseling and the relation of ministers and doctors in their co-operative ministry to the sick. These seminars have been conducted each summer since 1945. Normally they draw clergymen from a variety of denominations who live in cities and towns in widely separate parts of the country. The courses must be limited to about twenty-five students because considerable personal clinical supervision is included.

At the conclusion of each summer seminar, the students attend an evaluation session where they are asked to comment on the course and offer ways to improve it for the following summer. During the evaluation session in the summer of 1957 one of the students, a pastor from Kokomo, said, "This seminar has been tremendously helpful to me. I believe it will significantly change my perception of my responsibilities and opportunities of service to my people. But if I am to follow through on some of these necessary changes in myself, I will need the daily encouragement of fellow pastors who also feel as I do. As long as I have been surrounded by these men in the seminar, I have been doing quite well in my resolution to change. But when I get back to Kokomo, my enthusiasm will probably be dampened by the fact that I will have no one to talk to about these matters." He concluded by saying, "I wish that every minister in Kokomo could have taken this course."

The pastor from Kokomo touched off an animated discussion. Every man present said approximately the same thing. Courses like this would have cumulative value if the students were all from the same community, for they could work together in implementing these newer concepts of clinical theology.

During the next few months we at the university did a good deal of thinking and planning on the possible development of such a project. With the help of Lilly Endowment, Inc. we finally decided to go to Kokomo and invite all full-time clergymen to attend such a seminar. We gave it the general title of "The Role of the Clergyman in Mental Health." Through the help of various groups in Kokomo and particularly the Kokomo *Tribune*, we were able to explain the nature of the project to this community of some forty thousand people. There were approximately thirty-five full-time clergymen in Kokomo and surrounding Howard County. Of this number twenty-three responded to the invitation.

We changed the format of the usual two-week summer course and separated each of the two weeks by a period of six months, during which time the clergymen were to meet together in Kokomo for monthly four-hour clinical sessions to discuss cases having teaching value. The Kokomo project was jointly sponsored by the Department of Religion and Health with the assistance of the Department of Psychiatry. Dr. Edgar Draper, a psychiatrist, gave full time to the project during each of the one-week sessions. Chaplain Carl E. Wennerstrom of the University of Chicago Clinics and I acted as directors of the project.

It was not long after the arrival on our campus of the twenty-three Kokomo pastors that we were convinced of the value of inviting *all* the clergymen of a particular community to study the force of joint clergy action in the area of pastoral care and mental health. The Kokomo group consisted of a cross section of the major Protestant denominations as well as some less known denominations like Bible Baptist, Independent, and Mennonite. A Roman Catholic priest was in the group but there was no rabbi, for Kokomo had no resident rabbi at the time. We were fortunate that Dr. John Hoyt, a newly arrived psychiatrist in Kokomo, was able to participate in the entire project. He lived with the clergymen in the dormitory on the campus. This was his first experience in such a setting, and he said it afforded him an unusual opportunity to get to know the men informally.

By the end of about the third day many of the clergymen began talking freely about their reactions to this experiment. Some of them admitted that they had not wanted to come to this seminar but were practically forced to attend by members of their churches who, upon reading the newspaper articles, had insisted they take advantage of this unusual opportunity. These men had tried to beg off, pleading too much work, but their parishioners won out. They admitted that during the first day they had resisted becoming involved in the small group discussions of actual case situations. They said that as they gradually realized that the teachers held parish pastors in high regard they had found themselves more willing to enter into the discussions.

Then these pastors described "bull sessions" lasting far into the night in which they began to explore possible ways they might utilize some of the new insights for the good of Howard County. As they learned to appreciate one another in the neutral setting of the university campus, away from the arena of competition, they vowed no longer to compete against each other.

These men were kept very busy from early morning until late at night in large groups, in small groups, and in individual consultation. An attempt was made to cover certain areas and subjects which they could use as background for their clinical work in Kokomo during the six months before they returned to the campus for the second week of intensive study. In these sessions considerable time was spent in describing the process of personality development and how they might detect early signs of mental illness in children. Also discussed was the family and ways in which the clergyman might assist in getting families off to a good start, particularly since he assumes this responsibility in agreeing to marry couples. The importance of the pastor's conversation with his people was stressed. In this group, as in others, it was found that the pastors felt very ineffective as counselors. All of them said that although increasing numbers of people were coming to them with their problems, they felt there was little they could do for them. One of the aims of the first week of the course was to give these students a new appreciation of how helpful a pastor can be to people by carefully listening to them.

Following the first week of intensive study on the campus, all the men agreed to meet monthly for clinical discussions in Kokomo. The first of these sessions fell on an unusually hot day in July, and the teachers who went down from Chicago were certain that the attendance would be poor. Instead, however, they found close to forty pastors awaiting them. Every pastor in the county now wanted to be in on this project. But the difficulty lay in the fact that a special psychological testing program had been begun with the original group and to bring in so many new men would invalidate the testing process. Reluctantly, the newcomers were dismissed and discussions continued for the next six months with regular meetings of about four hours in length. During these months some smaller groups also met on their own to study certain books and to discuss specific problems facing them in their parishes.

These monthly meetings were followed by a second week of study on the campus of the University of Chicago. Each man was assigned a section of the hospital where he functioned as a student chaplain for two hours a day. Following his floor duty he met with a small group, including his fellow students and an instructor, in which he was helped to analyze his work. During this week the discussion dealt particularly with the psychodynamics of illness as these are related to typical parishioner troubles. Also employed were role playing and case presentations to demonstrate pastoral counseling methods. These were shown to have their roots in the essential doctrines of the Christian faith which first must be understood before effective help can be given. Another important consideration was the need of modern man to have a person he respects with whom he can discuss his sense of guilt. The Protestant ministers agreed that such a service should be provided and that there ought to be a re-examination of the place of the confessional in modern society. Throughout the week students found that they were re-examining basic doctrines of their faith, particularly those of sin and grace, confession and absolution, love and justice. They were made aware of the importance of an understanding of these concepts as they are related to health or its absence.

When the second week was nearly over and an evaluation session was held, it was the unanimous request of the group that the Kokomo project be continued for at least another six months and that from this point on the other pastors in the community be invited to participate. It was further decided that in addition to the regular clinical meeting each month, certain professional groups from Kokomo be invited to sit in to discuss common problems.

These meetings were held with other professional groups and were found to be most helpful, as it proved to be the first time that the lawyers, the physicians, and the educators had ever sat down with the ministers of the community to discuss specific ways in which they could co-operate in matters of community health and welfare. The ministers said that as a result of these meetings, it was much easier for them to talk with these professional people concerning matters pertaining to their parishioners.

After one year the Kokomo project was technically over, except for the results of the psychological tests, which over a period of years will seek to determine whether any changes are observable in the pastors who participate. These changes have to do with their ability to detect early signs of mental illness and

make appropriate referral; to improve the quality of their counseling with individuals under stress, and to work co-operatively
with physicians and other professional people in joint projects
related to community health.

The results of testing seventeen out of twenty-three men in
the project several months after the first week on the campus
caused the psychologist on the project, Dr. Andrew Mathis, to
describe his findings in this way:

"The Kokomo project seems to have accomplished something
significant. . . . The sense of isolation from which many of them
seemed to have moved should begin to show in their parish contacts. . . . From pre- to post-testing there was an increased tendency to be more accepting of emotionality. In terms of behavior,
it would indicate that these men have moved toward being more
capable of accepting an emotional stimulus for what it is without
having to alter it immediately to suit their own terms. . . . There
was, along with this increased acceptance of emotionality, a decrease in the introduction of fight and flight. This is an impres-
sive change. It suggests a greater tolerance for a broad range of
emotional relatedness and a decreasing tendency to alter de-
fensively the emotional climate of an interaction either by directly opposing it or withdrawing from it. The extent to which
these responses reflect a real change in their behavior should
contribute toward increased effectiveness with a wider group
of people. . . . Further, these men showed that they are more
accepting and understanding of the need of others who exhibit
avoidance behavior (increased acceptance of flights), but less
inclined to initiate avoidance (flight) behavior themselves."

Before the year was over, the ministers of Kokomo began an
interesting experiment in education for marriage. Most of them
asked couples who wished to be married by them to participate
in a course conducted several times each year on an all-county
basis. Church bulletins carried an announcement that couples
desiring to be married in the church were expected to get in
touch with the pastor at least one month prior to the date of the
wedding so that he might get to know each couple personally.
As a result of this tightening up of standards for Christian mar-

riages, couples are now calling the pastor as much as *six* months prior to the date of the ceremony to arrange for counseling and instruction. Kokomo pastors are more convinced than ever that young people today want to take marriage more seriously if only their elders will provide a worth-while discipline which will help them prepare for it.

The Kokomo project is continuing on its own power, which is as it should be. The pastors are now trying to formalize certain features of the project under the Howard County Council of Churches. There is particular interest in the case conference format through which physicians, lawyers, social workers, and ministers can seek to work through actual problems as they occur in the lives of individuals and families of the community. If such a pattern succeeds, it will be the first time that so large a percentage of clergy of any city are involved in a program of co-operative service to individuals and the community.

As we look over the one-year period, we think of some of the objectives toward which such a project points. Here are ten of them:

1. *To introduce parish clergy to the intensive university-level education which is now available in the field of pastoral theology.* A number of the Kokomo men indicated that they were unaware of such clinical courses. Others said that although they had heard of them, they were hesitant to apply because they were not sure they could qualify. Still others said they thought that a theological seminary or university could not speak to the needs of parish pastors. As a result of the course they now believe that post graduate education can be made relevant for the parish pastor and that it is both possible and necessary that any course which stresses clinical procedures be related closely to theological content. The Kokomo men expressed the hope that the University of Chicago and other theological or medical centers would offer further clinical seminars on other topics of concern to the practicing pastor. They mentioned such areas as religious education, preaching, social ethics, world religions, social work, functional illness, etc.

2. *To encourage other universities, colleges, theological and*

medical schools across the country to offer regular courses for clergy in clinical theology. The Kokomo project has demonstrated not only the interest of the typical parish pastor in this type of postgraduate course, but also the need to have several centers across the country where such courses can be offered on a regular basis for the benefit of clergy of all denominations.

3. *To seek clarification of the minister's role and responsibility in the search for underlying causes of mental illness.* If much mental illness has its roots deep in the early family life of the individual, then it is only right that the one profession which still makes calls in the home should be given access to the latest findings in the prevention and recognition of mental illness. It is an integral part of the pastor's professional activity to visit families regularly in their natural surroundings and to see them in the give-and-take of ordinary daily life. This unusual relationship can be of inestimable value in dealing with emotional crises within families of the parish and in discerning precipitating factors in mental illness.

4. *To prepare the clergy to recognize those emotional problems which have their roots in religious conflict.* Religion is concerned with meanings and basic attitudes toward life. What a person believes about life and his relation to his family, his fellows, and his Creator significantly determines his reaction to difficult life situations. The clergyman must understand when a person is using his religion for neurotic purposes and how to help the person move toward a healthier appropriation of religious faith. The pastor must also be sufficiently understanding about both normal and abnormal conflicts in marriage in order to assist couples to look objectively at the causes of marital deterioration. Pastoral counseling involves the responsibility of distinguishing between disturbances which are religious in origin and those brought on by other causes. In order to deal sensitively with emotional disturbances of many types, it is essential that the pastor be given special training in understanding the dynamics of human behavior.

5. *To demonstrate the importance of a co-operative attack on*

mental illness by fellowship and exchange among all members of the clergy in a particular community. Clergymen tend to work independently. They have not developed a program like the doctors' case conference for exchanging experiences and the discussion of new insights. They have never quite caught the physician's vision of the team approach in the understanding and care of people. I believe the Kokomo project has shown that when a group of ministers from the same community meet regularly for organized discussion of actual cases currently confronting them, their strengths and weaknesses can be more specifically noted to their own advantage. For too long the clergy have admitted only their successes to their colleagues; now our experiments with these pastoral "clinical pathological conferences" show the importance of admitting failures as well. Such clinical case conferences are seen as a possible additional feature of the regular monthly ministerial associations in even the smallest communities. Whenever experimental case conferences have been well-organized and conducted by a responsible committee, the clergy have shown a willingness to add this extra hour to their monthly meetings.

6. *To relate clergymen to other professional groups working in the area of health.* The Kokomo project sought to relate the clergy to other professional people in the community with whom close co-operation would be mutually beneficial. While a few clergy had done this on their own, it remained for a community-wide project to implement it. For example, a number of professional people had resisted previous requests from individual clergymen for interprofessional co-operation. Later when the project had been carefully explained to each of these professional groups and there had been opportunity for discussion, the resistance was reduced to a minimum.

7. *To encourage pastors to promote an ongoing educational program in their own churches related to mental and spiritual health.* Every local congregation lends itself well to a continuing program of education through small group discussions and personal counseling. Because the congregation includes all age

groups, it is possible to grade the educational programs to the particular needs of special groups. The pastor can put his own time to best use by carefully training several laymen who can lead small groups in discussions of problems unique to them. This gives the pastor more opportunity to work with those parishioners who desire personal counseling.

8. *To consider an organized program of continuing postgraduate education for the parish pastor in a variety of areas.* I have been inspired by the program of continuing education for general practitioners organized by the American Academy of General Practice to consider whether a similar program could be arranged for parish pastors. It is to be hoped that the American Association of Theological Schools might arrange such continuing postgraduate courses for ministers-in-practice as being within the purview of its function and responsibility.

Little or no provision has been made by theological seminaries for parish ministers to continue their study of clinical aspects of theology. The only opportunities now available for postgraduate training utilize the traditional methods of occasional lectures delivered to hundreds of clergymen at once rather than the seminar type of clinical instruction. That such conferences are not filling the expressed needs of today's clergy is indicated by the growing number of requests for smaller clinical seminars on many subjects. The few seminars now being held do not begin to meet the needs of the vast numbers of clergy who would like to participate and who ought to become involved in this new dynamic educational process. Of the 350,000 clergymen in the United States, it is estimated that 325,000 have had little orientation in the area of clinical theology. This presents a formidable problem which could be corrected at least in part if a number of special teaching centers around the country could be designated as postgraduate educational programs for parish clergy.

9. *To discover how a cross section of American clergy with traditional courses in theology would respond to a radically different manner of teaching.* There was the expected initial resistance to the personal involvement of each student, and it

took a while before some of the men were willing to expose their own counseling ability in role-playing situations. When, however, a few of their colleagues were willing to stick their necks out, the humor of the situation helped to relieve the tension. I believe that all the men had their "armor" pierced at some point; but I am of the opinion that really to change past habits of clergymen will require regular courses in clinical theology throughout the clergyman's life—courses such as those described earlier.

10. *To help ministers find new insights for their own personal mental health.* A broad perspective for the continuing personal development of the participants was one of the primary goals. "Physician, heal thyself" applies here. In this age of constant change and anxiety the minister needs to develop new resources for his own mental health. If he is to be helpful to others, he must be somewhat aware of the unconscious dynamics of his own behavior. In view of the nature of the minister's commitment, perhaps he more than any other professional person needs to know how to deal with his own problems in such a way that he does not project them on to his people. His own problems must not obstruct a sensitive and responsible ministry to his people. This is particularly true since he has the unique opportunity of talking to his people uninterrupted in the sermon he preaches each week. All the more reason that he should have a mature understanding of what is going on in his own personal relationships.

These were the ten objectives of the Kokomo project. The "forgotten" parish pastor must be given the privilege of keeping abreast of the latest developments in pastoral care. The growing realization that physical and mental health are related to spiritual health makes it imperative that the clergyman be trained to comprehend the interrelationship. At present the physician and he are the professional people most strategically positioned to awaken the public to the many measures which can be utilized by the family, the school, and the church in averting many forms of illness.

The Kokomo project has enabled those who have been associated with it to perceive a little more clearly the vast potential for creative relationships between ministers and doctors and those in allied professions (many aspects of which have been discussed in this book). Ministers are eager to make a constructive contribution to everything related to sound community health. They are more receptive than we thought to self-criticism. They seem willing to learn better ways to minister to people. This has been shown not only by the Kokomo project but also by the growing attendance of ministers at other postgraduate courses across the country. The next two decades hold much promise for a significant change—almost a revolution—both in the theological education and in the quality of pastoral care with which ministers will meet the needs of their people.

The University of Chicago's next project, patterned after the Kokomo experience, is being carried on in La Grange, Illinois, a suburban community near Chicago. While the second project resembles Kokomo in many ways, several new features are being added. Specifically, the second project will center its activities around the local community hospital following the two one-week periods on the campus of the University of Chicago. The physicians of the community hospital have been invited to participate in the regular case presentation discussions to be held in the hospital. Most of the cases will be presented jointly by the patient's physician and pastor, and the members of the seminar will seek to bring the resources of both church and medicine to bear upon the problems presented. It is also hoped that the project will show that a typical community hospital can be used as a base for such interprofessional communication.

I believe that as people in the community learn of the willingness of doctors and clergymen to be taught by each other, a new confidence will be developed in both of these professions. Further, each professional person stands to gain in competence when he can with openness and humility be taught by a person who looks at health and illness in a different way.

INDEX

Index

Allergies, 50–51
Alvarez, Walter, 50
American Protestant Hospital Association, The, 70
Art of Ministering to the Sick, The, 5
Artificial insemination, 153
Association of Hospital Chaplains, organization of, 11

"Between interviews" program, 62–66
Birth control, 142–145; methods of, 145–146
Boggs, Wade H., Jr., 158 n.
Boisen, Anton T., 11, 12, 13
Brauer, Jerald, xi
Brinton, William, 49

Cabot, Richard C., 5, 12
Cannon, Walter B., 49
Cardiovascular system, psychosomatic disturbances of, 49–50
Case conferences: conclusions from, 90–91; teaching by, 82
Chaplain, hospital, 66; duties of, 68–70; patients of, 72–81; qualifications of, 67–68; report by, 7, 9; role of, interpreted to doctor, 106–113
Clergyman, *see* Minister
Clinical training program, 68
Coggeshall, Lowell T., xi
Cole, William G., 132
Communication, art of, 15; *see also* Conversation; Counseling
Conscience, 36, 37, 57; definition of, 35; overdeveloped, 37–40, 54; underdeveloped, 35–37, 39
Conversation, 103; as catharsis, 41–

42; pastoral, 138; value of, 128; *see also* Communication, art of; Counseling
Conversation, professional, *see* Counseling
Conversation, therapeutic, *see* Counseling
Council for Clinical Training, 12
Counseling: conversation as, 14; doctor's role in, 22–29; "don't's" for, 19–20; goal of, 17–18; helps for, 20–21; patient's role in, 24–26, 56–57; pitfalls of, 17, 18; place of, 62; role of teaching in, 18; time for, 34; *see also* "Between interviews" program; Communication, art of; Conversation; Pastoral care
Couples: engaged, 140–146; married, 146–154
Crying, releasing tension through, 43–44

Death, *see* Terminal illness
Decision-making, 37; area of, 34
Defeat, expressing feelings of, 44
Dicks, Russell L., 5, 12
Discipline, 37–38
Discouragement, expressing feelings of, 44
Doctor: case conference with minister, 82–90; role of, in therapy, 27–31
Draper, Edgar, 164
Dunbar, Helen Flanders, 50

Education, *see* Clinical training program; Marriage, education for; Minister, clinical training for; Pastoral care, training in; Sex education

177